ATOMIC ENERGY
THE FIRST HUNDRED YEARS

Other Books by Egon Larsen

ATOMIC ENERGY
THE FIRST HUNDRED YEARS

*The Intelligent Layman's Guide
to the Nuclear Age*

EGON LARSEN

A NEW BOOK EXPRESSLY WRITTEN FOR
PAN BOOKS LTD : LONDON

First published 1958 by
PAN BOOKS LIMITED
8 Headfort Place, London, S.W.1

Printed in Great Britain by Richard Clay and Company, Ltd.,
Bungay, Suffolk

CONTENTS

ILLUSTRATIONS
IN PHOTOGRAVURE

(between pages 96 and 97)

An aerial view of Calder Hall, the world's first full-scale nuclear power station, comprising stations A and B. Each station consists of two reactors with their heat exchangers, a turbine hall, and two cooling towers

No. 1 reactor of the Calder Hall A generating unit

A process worker in a protective 'Windscale suit' at Dounreay

Shippingport: America's first commercial nuclear power station. The tubing above the reactor contains automatic recording instruments

The Zero Energy Thermo-nuclear Assembly, (ZETA), at Harwell.

How the thermonuclear flame would look if one could see inside the torus

The six-million-volt electrostatic generator at Aldermaston, Britain's nuclear weapons centre

A concrete 'tunnel' under construction at the Brookhaven National Laboratory, U.S.A., which will house the magnet for a 25,000–30,000 million electron volt proton-synchroton

LINE DRAWINGS
IN THE TEXT

PREFACE

IN this book I have tried to cover the most important aspects of atomic energy, tracing its story back to the earliest beginnings and attempting to forecast some future developments.

Perhaps the reader will miss a chapter about present-day nuclear weapons. I have deliberately kept them out of my tale, for two reasons. First, any details about them are of course shrouded in the cloak of secrecy, and the reader's guess as to their shape and functioning would be as good as mine. Secondly, I am optimistic enough to believe that the military application of nuclear energy is but a passing phase, and that mankind will eventually triumph over its own suicidal mania. If these weapons were really used all book-writing and reading would come to a sudden end, together with the rest of civilization; if not, then there is hardly any point in describing these instruments of mass annihilation.

The publishers and I are very grateful indeed to the Chief Press Officer of the United Kingdom Atomic Energy Authority, Mr Stanley R. White, and its Scientific Press Officer, Dr H. Manley, for supplying me with much valuable information and picture material for this book, and for taking the trouble of looking through my manuscript to help me in keeping down to a minimum the possible errors in the treatment of a subject which is so highly complex. Thanks are also due to Mr W. A. Dunn, Editor of the *Atoms for Peace Digest* (United States Information Service, London) for his assistance with much essential information and picture material.

E. L.

I

SLEUTHS OF SCIENCE

ONE DAY in spring, 1898, an unusual letter arrived in the manager's office at the old silver mine of St Joachimsthal in Bohemia. There was never a heavy postbag for the mine, and rarely a letter from abroad; gone were the days when St Joachimsthal was Europe's greatest supplier of sterling silver and its coins were famous all over the world—people called them 'Joachimsthaler', later abbreviated to 'Taler' and, overseas, to 'dollar'.

But when the silver deposits were exhausted, the miners and the mint masters departed, and St Joachimsthal became deserted. With the growth of the chemical industry, a modest new business began in the place: the pitchblende in the mine was suitable for dye production, but the Austrian authorities did nothing to develop it, and the mine often hovered on the brink of a complete close-down. A miracle was necessary to make St Joachimsthal prosperous again.

The manager never dreamt that it was about to happen when he opened that letter with the Paris postmark.

The Shining Element

The writers were two young French scientists, Pierre and Marie Curie. They asked whether the management of the mine could let them have 10,000 kilograms of pitchblende—free of charge, for they could not afford to buy it. They said that they would be quite satisfied with slag, the residue left after the more valuable components had been extracted for the dye. They explained that they thought they had discovered some new element which could be found, in infinitesimally small quantities, in that pitchblende—to be more precise, in the uranium ore it contained. That element, they said in their letter, might have some scientific importance.

The manager shrugged his shoulders. The slag was usually shovelled into the river. Why not let these French people have the stuff?

It was put into a number of empty soda-barrels and sent off

to Nogent-sur-Marne, where M. and Mme. Curie worked in an old chemical factory which had been placed at their disposal by Baron Rothschild.

What kind of people were the Curies?

Marie, the daughter of a high-school professor, Sklodowsky, in Warsaw, had come to Paris as a student. Her teacher, the physicist Professor Becquerel, made her his assistant. For many years Becquerel had kept a few pieces of uranium ore from Bohemia in an unused drawer. One day Marie Sklodowska happened to weight some photographic plates with them. When the plates were developed they showed a strange network of veins—as if glow-worms had run across them.

There could be no doubt: something in the ore was giving off a yet unknown kind of rays. Professor Becquerel experimented with that mysterious radiation, and gave lectures on it. The term 'Becquerel rays' was coined. But not even the Professor himself suspected that this radiation was a phenomenon that might upset the whole foundation of natural science. He was a competent physicist, but perhaps he lacked one essential quality of a good research worker—imagination.

Marie Sklodowska, or rather Marie Curie since her marriage to a French scientist, Pierre Curie, possessed that quality. Marie talked to Pierre about her suspicion: that it was not the ore which gave off that strange radiation, but some other, yet unknown element, encased in extremely small quantities in it. Pierre, although sceptical, agreed to work with her on what was no more than a scientific hunch. Determined to discover the source of the 'Becquerel rays', she gave up her post as the Professor's assistant, and the couple moved to Nogent-sur-Marne. They examined a geological map of Europe. Where could they get a large amount of uranium ore for their experiments? Their searching fingers stopped at the little dot indicating St Joachimsthal, and they wrote their letter.

The pitchblende arrived, and the work began. In order to find that hidden element—for Marie was now sure it did exist—the stuff had to be liquefied and boiled down. Day and night, for weeks and months, Pierre and Marie did the strenuous work of stirring it with heavy poles in enormous buckets. What remained was first filled into pots, and eventually into rows of glass bowls. Still Marie thought that it was not yet concentrated sufficiently, and in the end there was just one little test-tube containing some whitish liquid.

One night in November, 1898, the alarm-clock rang in the shed near the laboratory to wake the Curies, who had lain down for a few hours' rest. It was three o'clock in the morning: the liquid must have crystallized by now, and they would at last be able to see the new element—*their* element. The crowning moment of their work had come; out of 10,000 kg of uranium pitchblende the first few grains of a new substance had been won. What would it look like?

They opened the laboratory door—and stopped on the threshold. From one corner of the dark room came a faint, unearthly, mysterious, bluish light: it was a fantastic sight, almost frightening.

As they lit the gas lamp the bluish light vanished, and there was nothing but a little test-tube containing one-tenth of a gram of an off-white salt.

The Curies decided to call it 'radium', the Shining Element.

The 'Indivisible' Atom

The brilliant scientific work which led to the discovery of the element radium might never have been carried out if Marie Curie had accepted the current notions about the structure of matter. But she questioned them, and in doing so she completely upset the scientific apple-cart.

For over 2000 years the philosophers had believed that everything on earth consisted of very small, indivisible particles called atoms—indeed, the Greek word *atomos* means indivisible. The idea was first put forth by the Greek scientist Democritus, who lived in the 5th century BC. There was, of course, no possibility of proving that notion by experiment, and only towards the end of the 18th century did the development of experimental chemistry lead to more thorough research into the theory of the atom.

An English chemist, John Dalton, showed that all types of matter, living or dead, are made up of a relatively small number of basic substances, the 'elements', and that each element has its special kind of atom. Dalton's 'Atomic Theory' explained that the atoms of the elements tend to combine to form what we call molecules, or clusters of atoms; these molecules may consist of atoms of the same element or of different elements: thus, atoms of oxygen and hydrogen combine to form molecules of water; carbon, hydrogen, and oxygen integrate into compounds called carbohydrates—sugar,

11

starch, cellulose; oxygen, nitrogen, and some other gases make up the air we breathe. The way in which the atoms of the various elements join each other to form molecules, their respective numbers, the pattern of their combination are responsible for all the innumerable varieties of matter, living or dead, animal, mineral, or vegetable.

We can change these combinations, and in fact Life is nothing but an endless series of chemical reactions. Molecules are broken up, and the atoms of which they consist made to combine with others in some other way—whether the plants produce their sugar and starch from water and carbon dioxide with the help of sunlight, or petrol is turned into a force that drives a motor-car; whether we are digesting our food, or taking a photograph: all the time chemical changes are going on, which means that atoms are added, shed, or re-arranged in the molecules.

When Dalton developed that theory of the structure of matter towards the end of the 18th century he assumed, with Democritus, that the atom is the smallest particle of a substance, and that the atom of one element differs from that of another mainly in weight. Throughout the 19th century scientists added to the list of elements until they arrived at the figure of 92, from the lightest, the gas hydrogen, to the heaviest, the metal uranium. They prided themselves on their enlightened conception of the immutability of the elements— lead was lead, and remained lead, and could never be changed into gold, as the mediæval alchemists believed it could.

Until that night in November, 1898, when the Curies saw their strange new element for the first time, there was hardly any doubt that atoms were anything else but solid, minute billiard balls of matter, unchangeable and indivisible. But the new phenomenon, the shining element radium, made nonsense of that traditional notion. For the faint light it gave off was a constant stream of matter, of particles smaller than the atom, 'radiating' from it; clearly, the whitish stuff in the test-tube was disintegrating, it was changing into something else, its atoms were breaking up. The Curies were able to calculate that within the space of 1600 years half of any given quantity of radium disappears—to be more accurate: half of its matter turns into radiation. And what is radiation? Nothing but energy.

Small wonder that scientists everywhere felt the ground

give way under their feet when they read of Marie Curie's discovery. So the atom was neither immutable, nor was it the smallest existing particle of matter. What was matter? What was energy? the scientists had to ask themselves anew. Could one really change into the other?

As Marie and Pierre Curie examined the way in which the disintegration of their element was going on, they laid the foundation of the modern theory of atomic structure.

The Skeleton Hand

There were other pointers towards a fundamental re-orientation in scientific thought. Three years before the discovery of radium a German physicist, Professor Wilhelm Konrad Röntgen, carried out a series of experiments on the conduction of electricity in gases. He used an instrument which had been invented by an English scientist, Sir William Crookes, and was therefore called 'Crookes's Tube'—better known today under the name of cathode-ray tube. It was a sealed glass tube with two metal plates called electrodes; when they were connected to a battery of sufficiently high voltage there was an electric discharge from the negative electrode, or 'cathode', to the positive electrode, the 'anode'.

As long as there was air in the tube the discharge took the form of a spark; but when the air was nearly all pumped out of the tube there was a kind of diffuse glow. This was something unexpected: it seemed that the electric current found it easier to pass from the cathode to the anode in a constant, regular stream when there was no air. Crookes made the experiment, which Röntgen repeated, of putting an obstacle—a metal shield in the form of a little star—in the tube between the two electrodes to see whether it would throw a shadow. And it did indeed; the shadow of the star appeared on the opposite wall of the glass tube. This proved that whatever caused the glow must be a stream of particles, or some kind of light-rays, moving in a straight line. But what were they really? For want of a better name they were called 'cathode-rays'.

Röntgen tried out all kinds of devices. One day he put the tube in a cardboard box to see if the glow would penetrate it. Suddenly his gaze fell on a screen with fluorescent coating, which was lying near the cardboard box, left over from some previous experiment. The screen had lit up, emitting a greenish glow. So the cathode-rays were penetrating not only the glass of the tube but also the cardboard—there was no other explanation. When Professor Röntgen switched off the current the fluorescent screen went dark: when he turned the current on it lit up again. It must be that these cathode-rays were some kind of invisible light, he thought; and where there's light there must be a shadow. He held his hand between the box and the screen to see if it would cast a shadow—and snatched it back as if some poisonous snake had stung it!

Was it hallucination? Had his nerves played him a trick?

He thought that, for the flash of a moment, he had seen a skeleton hand on the screen, the eerie shadow of his own hand. After a moment of hesitation, he thrust his hand out again, and there was the skeleton shadow! He could see his own bones, with the flesh and skin forming a thin, greyish fringe around them.

Professor Röntgen's amazement turned into triumph. By accident he had discovered a new kind of rays: invisible rays which could penetrate solid matter such as flesh and skin but not bones; he found that they went through wood but not through metal. They would enable Man to see the inside of things, living or dead.

Being a modest scientist, he called them not after himself but named them X-rays because of their mysterious nature. It did not take him long to find out how they were produced: when the cathode-rays struck a material object such as the metal shield in the tube, they turned into X-rays; and he found that they affected a photographic plate in a way similar to light rays. One of the first experiments he made was to photograph his own skeleton hand.

Electrons in the Cloud Chamber

These were profoundly disturbing phenomena, and the physicists had to admit that they would have to make a fresh start. Dalton's indivisible little sphere, the traditional conception of the atom, was on its way out.

It was Professor (later Sir) Joseph John Thomson who opened the doors of the Cavendish Laboratory, Cambridge, to research students from all over the world for the purpose of investigating the microcosm of the atom. In 1895 the short, dark-haired physicist, then in his fortieth year, was joined by a tall, young, moustached New Zealander, a farmer's son by the

14

name of Ernest Rutherford, who soon became Thomson's closest collaborator.

They repeated Röntgen's experiments. 'You know, one can see the bones of the hand and arm with the naked eye,' Rutherford wrote to his mother at home. 'The method is very simple. A little bulb is exhausted of air and an electrical discharge sent through. The bulb then lights up and looks of a greenish colour. The X-rays are given off and if a piece of cardboard, with a certain chemical on it, is held near it, metal objects placed behind can be seen through several inches of wood!'

But what were these cathode-rays and X-rays really? That was the question which Thomson set out to answer, and one evening in the spring of 1897 he was able to inform his students: "Cathode-rays are particles of negative electricity." And he gave them their name: 'electrons'. X-rays, however, were found to be electro-magnetic waves of the same type as light, but of a much shorter wavelength. Somewhere between the two was that mysterious borderline between matter and energy.

Even before Marie Curie announced the discovery of radium, Thomson and Rutherford experimented with Becquerel's uranium rays. Rutherford found that they were, in fact, of three types. One could be stopped by a sheet of thick paper, but the second was much more powerful; he called them 'alpha rays' and 'beta rays'. When a piece of uranium was placed between the poles of a magnet and a photographic plate held above a slit, two images appeared on the plate: one could see how one kind of rays had been deflected by the magnet, while another kind bent only slightly: they must, therefore, be particles of matter, one with greater weight than the other. And then there was the third kind of rays, the 'gamma' type; they went straight on, unaffected by the magnet. Rutherford concluded that they were not particles but electro-magnetic waves similar to the X-rays, but with an even shorter wavelength.

Then came an astonishing discovery—that those beta particles were really fast-moving electrons, particles of negative electricity. These electrons kept appearing in all kinds of connections; it became obvious that they must be among the basic parts that constituted the atom: for the 20th century of Science began with the certainty that the atom was a system of various types of particles. There was, of course, no microscope powerful enough to make them visible. The scientists had to work like detectives pursuing a criminal: he had done this and that, left his marks and clues, and the experienced criminologists might form a picture of what he was like, or even predict what he would do in certain circumstances. But the sleuths of Science had not yet set eyes on him.

"I wish we could photograph the electron," J. J. Thomson said to his assistant, C. T. R. Wilson, one day. Wilson's reply was to invent his famous 'cloud chamber': a glass chamber was filled with dust-free air and water vapour, and when an electron was sent through, it served as a nucleus for condensation of water droplets; its path could be seen and photographed as a thin, misty streak.

Here, for the first time, was a visible record of a sub-atomic particle!

Portrait of an Atom

In 1901 Rutherford joined forces with a twenty-three-year-old Englishman, Frederick Soddy, in Montreal. Together they worked out a theory explaining the phenomenon of radio-activity—of the rays emanating from uranium and radium. They suggested that radio-activity was due not only to a continuous breaking-up of atoms, but even of elements changing into other elements: thus, radium was ultimately turning into lead when its radio-activity was exhausted. That theory gave many of their fellow-scientists 'a rude shock', as Rutherford put it. He investigated the alpha particles more closely and came to the conclusion that they were helium atoms, but somehow they had each lost an electron and carried, therefore, a positive electric charge. He called them 'ions'. He was quite fond of them. "Ions are such jolly little beggars," he used to say. "You can almost see them!"

Rutherford's sayings became famous. Once he declared that a pound of the 'emanation' of radium, if it could be caught and utilized, would produce energy at the rate of 10,000 hp. He had established the fact that radium continually gave off heat, and his remark was the first hint by a scientist that the energy of the disintegrating atom might be of practical use. But he also said (was it one of his jokes, or a serious warning?) that "some fool in a laboratory might blow up the universe unawares".

Little by little the picture of the atom grew in Rutherford's mind like a jigsaw puzzle. Returning to England in 1907, where he took up a post at Manchester University, he worked with a young Danish scientist, Niels Bohr; the result was what used to be called the 'Rutherford—Bohr Atom'. "One day in 1911," one of their Manchester colleagues recalled, "Rutherford, obviously in the best of spirits, came into my room and told me that he now knew what the atom looked like!"

The scientific sleuths had tracked their quarry down. All the known facts fitted, if it was assumed that the atom consisted of a central core or nucleus, carrying a positive electric charge, and, revolving around it in various orbits, a number of negatively charged electrons. Almost the whole 'mass' of the atom is contained in the nucleus, which is composed of 'protons'—the carriers of the positive charge—and neutral 'neutrons'. (In 1911 Rutherford only suspected the existence of these particles, which were later identified and named; others have since been added to the list of those contained in the nucleus, such as the 'meson', which is assumed to act as a kind of atomic glue, holding the nucleus together.)

The electrons have next to no mass. They rotate around the nucleus like little planets around a sun. Their number, which is the same as that of the protons in the nucleus, varies from one element to another; this is called the 'atomic number'. This was, perhaps, the most amazing revelation of the Rutherford–Bohr portrait of the atom: that the whole difference between the various elements is the number of their protons and electrons. The lightest element, hydrogen, has one proton (and one electron revolving around it); uranium, the heaviest, has 92. Rutherford aroused a good deal of ridicule and opposition among his colleagues when he said that the transformation of one element into another was not only possible—by removing or adding protons—but taking place in Nature all the time.

Because the number of positively charged protons in the nucleus is the same as that of the negatively charged electrons revolving around it, an atom is normally electrically neutral—the charges cancel each other out. "The conclusion is unavoidable", said Rutherford, "that the atom is the seat of an intense electric field." Both X-rays and radium rays, he found, knock electrons off atoms, thus disturbing their electrical

17

balance and turning them into ions, atoms with an electric charge.

The atomic nucleus is extremely small, and there are vast empty spaces between the nucleus and the electrons revolving in their orbits. If we could enlarge an atom a millionfold it would be about as big as a full stop; but if we wanted to see the nucleus we would have to enlarge the whole atom another 20,000 times until it would become as big as a railway truck—and then the nucleus would be just about visible!

By the ingenious use of electro-magnets of different strengths the scientists were able to calculate the weight of an electron; it was found to be infinitesimal: about $1/1840$ of the weight of a hydrogen atom. Every electron weighs exactly the same, and carries the same amount of electricity. Later it was discovered that there are electrons also in the nucleus—at least that they shoot out of radio-active nuclei. Perhaps they are something else before they are ejected? We do not know; in fact, we know little about the state of the nucleus, about the way in which its particles hang together.

Frederick Soddy made another astonishing discovery. He found that any element could have a number of varieties, identical in all chemical and most physical properties and with the same atomic number (that is, the number of protons and electrons), but different atomic weight. He called these variations from the 'standard' atom isotopes. The different isotopes of an element contain different numbers of neutrons—electrically uncharged particles of the nucleus, slightly heavier than the protons. (We shall return later to the story of their discovery.) Nearly all elements in Nature are mixtures of several isotopes: oxygen and tin, uranium and hydrogen, to mention only a few; these isotopes are either lighter or heavier than the ordinary element. There is, for instance, a light isotope of uranium—and a heavy one of hydrogen.

When Soddy, at the age of twenty-three, first wondered what caused uranium to give off radiation, he could not have foreseen that the answer to this question would one day change the face of the earth. He found that ordinary uranium, atomic weight 238, is mixed with very small quantities of its lighter variety, U-235, which is unstable and breaks up, giving off what Professor Becquerel first observed as that mysterious radiation which affected his photographic plates. And no one could have foreseen the importance which heavy hydrogen

18

would gain half a century later. Hydrogen, atomic weight 1, always contains a minute percentage of 'deuterium', or heavy hydrogen, atomic weight 2, an isotope which has one neutron with its proton in the nucleus, and thus twice the mass of ordinary hydrogen: there is an even heavier and rarer isotope, 'tritium', with thrice the nucleus mass. These isotopes occur in ordinary water, that is, small quantities of 'heavy water' are mixed with the water in the sea and in the lakes and rivers of the earth.

To-day, heavy water has become of vital importance in the utilization of nuclear energy, and heavy hydrogen is the main constituent of the hydrogen bomb. Soddy's achievement in discovering the isotope was all the more brilliant as it was made twenty years before the discovery of the neutron.

'The Atom has Been Split'

"The experiments started about four in the afternoon," recalled a scientist whom Rutherford, Sir J. J. Thomson's successor at the Cavendish, had invited one day in 1919 to see what he was doing. "We went into his laboratory to spend a preliminary half hour in the dark to get our eyes into the sensitive state necessary for counting. Sitting there drinking tea, in the dim light of a minute gas jet at the further end of the laboratory, we listened to Rutherford talking of all things under the sun. It was curiously intimate yet impersonal, and all of it coloured by that characteristic of his of considering statements independently of the person who put them forward."

Then Rutherford, in his unassuming white coat, made a last-minute inspection tour round his laboratory, a high and wide room with a cement floor. There was, in one corner, the enormous column of the condenser, which went right up through the ceiling, and at another end of the room a large tube, enthroned on top of a workbench in the midst of a mass of entangled electric wires. There was an arc-lamp projector behind the tube, and a screen had been set up in front of it.

"You know, we might go up through the roof," warned Rutherford, but the boyish smile under the big greying moustache belied his words. The blinds were now pulled down over the big leaded windows, and bluish-green sparks were seen to jump to and fro in the tube. The screen lit up. At first there was nothing but a thick grey mist. Then some

19

large objects, like the shadows of enormous fish, flowed across the screen in a steady stream.

The Professor explained. Alpha particles—helium nuclei—were being hurled through the tube, in which an artificial mist had been created: it was an adaptation of Wilson's cloud chamber, filled with nitrogen gas. Suddenly a thick streak appeared on the screen, striking off at right angles at terrific speed.

"That's it," said Rutherford. "The atom has been split."

The performance was repeated—once, twice, a third time at irregular intervals. Millions of alpha particles went straight through the nitrogen gas without touching any of its atoms; but now and then there came a direct hit on a nitrogen nucleus, which split it.

"Where are we going from here?" mused one of Rutherford's guests.

"Who knows?" he replied. "We are entering no-man's land."

What interested Rutherford in these experiments was the transmutation of one element into another—which furnished the proof that his theory of what the atom looked like was correct. When an alpha particle hit a nitrogen nucleus it drove out some of its seven protons; and each of these loose protons became the nucleus of a hydrogen atom, which has only one proton with an electron revolving around it. Thus nitrogen changed into hydrogen!

But Rutherford proved yet another theory, which was closely connected with Einstein's hotly disputed claim: that there is no real difference between mass and energy, and that the destruction of matter would free its latent energy. Already in 1905 Albert Einstein, then a young man of 26, employed by the Patent Office in Bern as a technical expert, had startled the scientific world with his *Special Theory of Relativity*, in which he gave the phenomenon of radio-activity an important place within the framework of his new picture of the universe. He explained that if matter is converted into energy by the disintegration of atoms, that process would be represented by a simple little equation: $E = mc^2$.

What does it mean? Basically, it says that mass and energy are not, as it was generally assumed throughout the ages, different things which have no relation to one another—but that one can be changed into the other. Einstein's equation connects the two quantities. 'E' is the energy in ergs [1] released when a mass of 'm' grams is completely disintegrated; 'c' is the velocity of light in centimetres per second (30,000 millions), and therefore c^2 is 900 million million millions ergs.

This sounded completely fantastic. Even if matter could ever be converted into energy, argued the scientists, surely the energy released in this process would not be of such unimaginable magnitude! There was, of course, no way of proving or disproving Einstein's equation—until Rutherford showed how to split the atom.

It was he who confirmed the equation, which until then had been little more than a scientific puzzle without any practical meaning. If all the nuclear particles which had flown off after one of Rutherford's atomic collisions could have been put together again there would have been a piece missing from the nucleus: it had vanished completely—it had transformed itself into pure energy.

In 1905 no one really believed that Einstein's equation would ever be put to the test; that Man could ever release the incredible forces locked up in the atoms of matter. Today we know that if one ounce of matter could be completely destroyed and changed into energy it would yield as much power as we derive from burning 100,000 tons of coal in a conventional power station! But that would necessitate the thorough destruction of each atom. How many atoms are there in an ounce of, say, uranium? The number would be roughly the same as the number of grains of sand in the upper 150 yds of the entire Sahara desert.

Discovery of the Neutron

'Atom-splitting' became almost a fashion in the physical laboratories of Europe and America, and in the 1920s most of the lighter nuclei, being more vulnerable than those of the heavy elements, were being split by bombarding them with alpha particles. Only beryllium—the fourth-lightest of the elements—resisted all attempts to break up its nucleus. Instead of releasing one of its four protons when hit, it gave off a burst of radiation more penetrating than even the hard gamma

---

[1] Erg: unit of work = the work done by a force of 1 dyne acting through a distance of 1 cm. Dyne: unit of force = the force which, acting upon a mass of 1 gram, will impart to it an acceleration of 1 cm per second per second.

rays. Sir James Chadwick, again at the Cavendish Laboratory in Cambridge, proved that this radiation must consist of particles about as heavy as protons, but without an electric charge. "If such a neutral particle exists," Rutherford had said in 1920, "it should be able to move freely through matter, and it may be impossible to contain it in a sealed vessel." He knew that its discovery would be of great importance—an electrically neutral particle could be fired into any matter without its being attracted or repelled by protons or electrons.

Frédéric Joliot, a young French scientist, and his wife Irène, the daughter of Pierre and Marie Curie, were the first to provide experimental evidence that such a neutral particle really existed—more, that it was found in every nucleus except the ordinary hydrogen nucleus. In 1932 the Joliot-Curies made a radio-active metal bombard the recalcitrant beryllium, which is a non-radio-active metal, with its rays. The result was that the beryllium, too, became radio-active—even more so than the original source of the rays! Sir James Chadwick's explanation was that the beryllium nuclei had released their non-electrical particles, which he called neutrons. They were found to have a slightly greater mass than the protons—but neutrons can change into protons by acquiring a positive electric charge.

The discovery of the neutron not only solved quite a number of problems which had so far defied the efforts of the scientists, but it also gave an even greater impetus to atom-splitting experiments. The Americans, true to style, went into the business in a big way. The University of California built an enormous machine, the 'cyclotron', for the head of its radiation laboratory, Professor E. O. Lawrence, who had come to the conclusion that the heavy hydrogen atom, consisting of one proton plus one neutron, would make an ideal bullet for shooting up other nuclei. The cyclotron was designed as a device for imparting great velocity to these 'bullets'.

It is based on a simple idea: if you want to make a swing move you give it a series of little pushes, each of them increasing the movement, until the heavy swing reaches the greatest possible height. In the cyclotron, electrically charged atoms—ions—are made to rotate between the flat pole pieces of a strong electromagnet, which gives them a series of pushes in the form of shocks of alternating current until the highest possible speed—which means energy—is reached; then they are released, and shoot out at the target.

Strangely enough, however, the really great advances in nuclear physics were achieved with simple, inexpensive, home-made equipment. In 1932 two of Lord Rutherford's 'young men' at the Cavendish, John D. Cockcroft (now Sir John) and Dr E. T. S. Walton, built a simple machine, which looked more like a couple of stovepipes than an atom-smashing tool, for shooting electrically speeded-up protons at lithium atoms, using energies of more than 600,000 electron volts.[1] The result was that the lithium atoms split violently into nuclei of helium.

During all those years scientists in many countries went on bombarding atoms with particles and scoring occasional hits which told them something about the goings-on in that invisible microcosm; there was no question of any 'practical purpose', such as producing energy from the split nucleus. Besides, a great deal of work and preparation had to be invested in the business of smashing a measly few atoms. It all looked rather uneconomical; even Cockcroft's and Walton's discovery of the release of energy from the nuclei of light atoms did not point a short-cut to the atomic power station.

The Chain Reaction

During their experiments with radio-active bombardment of non-radio-active elements the Joliot-Curies had discovered that the bombarded nucleus often becomes unstable, that is, radio-active. This was the key that opened the gate to what is now the vast field of medical, industrial, agricultural, and research application of radio-active isotopes. The Italian scientist Enrico Fermi, working with a team of young assistants, produced within the short space of a few months a whole treasure chest of new radio-isotopes, one or more radio-active variations from a great number of elements, including, of course, uranium, which yielded more man-made isotopes than any other element—heavier varieties of uranium with atomic numbers beyond 92, the atomic number of ordinary uranium.

Fermi also discovered some surprising things, for instance the fact that neutrons could be slowed down by collisions with light atoms (*eg*, when they were made to pass through water)—and that their efficiency as missiles for splitting nuclei could be

[1] Electron-volt: unit of energy used in nuclear physics = the increase in energy of an electron when passing through a potential rise of 1 volt.

thus greatly *in*creased by *de*creasing their speed! Now, nearly every neutron was a 'hit' and would liberate some energy. Yet it was a wasteful and costly job to produce neutrons. It was in 1937, a short time before his death at the age of sixty-six, that Lord Rutherford remarked that he saw little chance of nuclear energy ever becoming a source of industrially usable power.

Then, however, things took an unexpected and decisive turn. The scene shifted to Germany. Professor Otto Hahn, a chemist who had worked with Sir William Ramsay and Lord Rutherford before settling down at the Kaiser Wilhelm Institute in Berlin, was somewhat sceptical about the discoveries claimed by the Joliot-Curies and the Fermi team. With his collaborators Strassmann and Dr Lise Meitner he set out to disprove those claims by repeating their experiments.

But when he bombarded uranium with neutrons he found, in fact, chemical substances which could not have been produced by any known atomic reaction. There was, for instance, a '13-minute body' (now called neptunium, one of the artificial transuranic elements), atomic number 93, which exhausted half its life within 13 minutes of radio-activity; also there were '23-minute bodies' and '3·5-hour bodies'. It was all very strange. Yet the strangest result of Hahn's experiments was that a substance produced by the neutron bombardment of uranium turned out to be barium, atomic number 56—that is, with 36 protons and electrons less than uranium.

Suddenly it dawned on him. There was only one possible explanation—the uranium nucleus must have broken into two parts, perhaps in the same manner in which living cells divide: by stretching, forming a 'waist', and then breaking up. The biologists call it 'fission'. Now if one of the nuclei was that of barium, with 56 protons, the other one must be that of krypton, a gas with 36 protons. Thus, both nuclei had a surplus of neutrons of which they would try to rid themselves. In other words: neutrons would be 'liberated'—and that meant energy!

Hahn, with Strassmann assisting, made the discovery of uranium fission shortly after Dr Lise Meitner had left the Institute and Berlin. She was an Austrian Jewess. Until March, 1938, the Nazi authorities had left her unmolested because she was a foreign national. But when Hitler marched into Vienna and annexed Austria, the anti-Jewish laws which had turned the German Jews into defenceless victims of Nazi

24

brutality were also applicable to Austrian Jews in Germany. Lise Meitner preferred not to wait until she was thrown out of her laboratory, but said farewell to Otto Hahn and fled to Stockholm.

Lise Meitner spent Christmas 1938 quietly in Stockholm with her nephew, Dr O. R. Frisch, also a physicist, now a professor in Cambridge. She showed him Professor Hahn's report on his experiments, which had just arrived. "At first I wouldn't listen to this; it seemed unbelievable," said Professor Frisch later. "But Lise Meitner insisted that Hahn was too good a chemist to be dismissed like that. Yet, how could it be? Could the impact of a neutron cause some dozen fragments to be broken off a uranium nucleus? The crudest estimate showed that this would need far too much energy. Could the nucleus be cleaved right across? This would involve cutting simultaneously a great many of the bonds by which the protons and the neutrons in the nucleus were held together; those bonds were known to be strong enough to exclude that possibility. Or could it be that the bonds were not cut all at once? Could the nucleus, as it were, be slowly pulled apart?"

Frisch remembered that Bohr had compared the nucleus to a drop of liquid whose parts are held together, like the molecules of water or oil, by strong forces. He took that notion a step farther: a drop might stretch, thin out, and finally divide in two. This must have happened when the neutron struck the uranium nucleus in Hahn's experiments. But what would happen next? There were two smaller nuclei, no longer held by the nuclear force, but pushed apart by electric repulsion, and flying off at very great speed. And such sudden display of energy would, according to Einstein's mass = energy equation, correspond to some loss of mass.

By an 'elegant experiment', as her nephew called it, Lise Meitner showed that practically the whole of the radioactivity produced by neutrons in uranium was due to fission fragments. When a uranium nucleus was torn in half, a few neutrons would be shaken loose, and make their way towards other nuclei; if they struck them they would cause further fissions!

It was again the Joliot-Curie team in Paris who proved experimentally in spring, 1939, that during the fission process of a uranium nucleus some neutrons were indeed liberated. The neutrons flew off, struck other nuclei, which in turn broke up, liberating more neutrons: and within an unbelievably short space of time a whole mass of uranium would break up in a 'chain' of fissions, not unlike the way in which one single snowball can start an avalanche. Enrico Fermi, who had left Italy in 1938 to escape life under Fascism and gone to America, was mainly responsible for working out the theory of what became known as chain reaction.

The Security Lid Slams Down

It was an amazingly small circle of scientists working towards the same goal in Europe and America, communicating chiefly by the reports on their achievements and discoveries they published in scientific journals, like a team of football players taking over the ball from one another. Fermi, continuing the train of thought of his European colleagues, realized that it was not just a matter of collecting some uranium and waiting for the first stray particle, perhaps one coming down from the sky with cosmic radiation, to start off that chain reaction. Ordinary uranium, U-238, would require very strong neutron bombardment to undergo fission, and it would be too stable to sustain a chain reaction. U-235, however, one of the uranium isotopes, is much less stable. It was the obvious material for the attempt at putting the theory of chain reaction into experimental practice; but the problem was how to separate the U-235 from the U-238.

Lise Meitner and Dr Frisch discussed the whole matter with Niels Bohr, who was on the point of departing for America for a short visit. There he talked to Albert Einstein, the 'grand old man' of physics, who had settled down at Princeton University. Einstein looked at the map of Europe and wrote a letter to President Roosevelt.

That letter, posted on August 2nd, 1939, set in motion the gigantic machinery which, exactly six years later, produced the horror of Hiroshima. Yet Einstein's intention was only to warn Roosevelt. The newly discovered phenomenon of chain reaction, he wrote, might be used for the development of bombs. In autumn, 1938, Hitler had been handed the Sudetenland on a platter by Chamberlain and Daladier at Munich; and in that part of Czechoslovakia there was a little town called St Joachimsthal, the centre of a mining region rich in uranium. If Hitler hit on the idea of producing a fission bomb he would have sufficient uranium at his disposal.

26

Already in 1936, in his Nobel speech, Professor Joliot had made this prediction: "When we look at the increasing tempo with which Science is progressing we may assume that the research workers, who are already able to build up or destroy elements, will learn to achieve changes of an explosive character, a chemical chain reaction. . . . We can visualize how tremendous this liberated, usable energy will be. But it might take hold of all the elements of our planet, and we must be wary of such a catastrophe. The astronomers observe from time to time the appearance of a Nova. The sudden flare-up of such a star may be caused by explosive transmutations. We can only hope that our scientists will take the necessary precautions when they begin to experiment with these phenomena."

The common people knew little about the scientists' efforts to achieve such 'explosive transmutations'. The Second World War broke out, and there were other things to worry about. Only occasionally some news paragraph from the sphere of Science found its way into the newspapers. There appeared, for instance, a curious story in a London daily four days before Hitler ended the 'phoney war' by attacking Holland, Belgium, and France (*Daily Telegraph*, May 6th, 1940):

NEW SOURCE OF POWER CLAIMED

U-235 Discovered by U.S. Scientists

From our own Correspondent

New York, Sunday.

The isolation of a new substance called U-235, a chemical twin of uranium, and a potential source of vast power, was announced by the *Physical Review* today. The discovery, it is claimed, may prove to be one of the greatest of modern science.

Predictions have already been made about the practical uses to which the new substance might be put if it could be isolated in pure form in comparatively large quantities. One pound, it is asserted, would be equal in power output to 5,000,000 lb of coal or 3,000,000 lb of petrol; and 5 or 10 lb would drive a liner or battleship without refuelling for a long period.

While uranium ore, in which the substance is present, is found in England, Canada, the Belgian Congo, Colorado and Germany, none of the substance had been isolated in pure

27

form until about two months ago. Even now only infinitesimal quantities have been obtained. Nevertheless, progress is reported, and it is suggested that within a few months a method of securing large quantities may be devised.

EFFECTS ON WAR

Already the implications the effect of this discovery might have on the outcome of the war have been discussed, and it is asserted that German physicists, chemists and engineers have been ordered to drop all other research and devote themselves to this aspect alone.

Germany, it is suggested, may regret having sent into exile Dr Lise Meitner, who, with Prof. Otto Hahn, made the first observations which led to the discovery. Soon after arrival in Stockholm Dr Meitner revealed the results of her work with Prof. Hahn to Prof. Niels Bohr, of the Copenhagen University. Prof. Bohr, a Nobel Prizeman in physics in 1922, immediately communicated them to American colleagues.

One of the most startling discoveries about U-235 is that energy can be liberated by pouring on it cold water, which promptly turns to steam. Thus, it is believed, the substance could be used by steamships without difficulty.

The newspaper's editor, understandably puzzled by this astonishing report from his New York correspondent, turned to a British scientist and asked him what he thought of the matter. The scientist's opinion appeared as a tailpiece to the American story:

BRITISH EXPERT'S VIEW

A London authority said last night that American claims concerning U-235 might well be true. The quantity available, however, was not likely to be one pound but perhaps a millionth of that amount. In his view, therefore, the discovery was unlikely to provide a secret weapon for either side in the war.

That was the last we heard about the 'New Source of Power'. The security lid slammed down, and nothing more was revealed for over five years while the atom bomb was being prepared behind the scenes of the Second World War.

II

MAN-MADE HELLFIRE

"THERE WAS a blinding flash lighting up the whole area brighter than the brightest daylight. Then came a tremendous, sustained roar and a heavy pressure wave which knocked down two men outside the control centre. Then a huge, multi-coloured, surging cloud boiled to an altitude of over 40,000 ft. The 100-ft steel tower was entirely vaporized. Where it had stood was a huge, sloping crater."

This was the description given by an official observer of the first atomic-bomb explosion in the New Mexico desert, where the bomb had been fixed to a steel tower. The observer at the control centre was watching from a distance of nearly ten miles.

The world knew nothing about it. The date was July 16th, 1945. The war in Europe was over; but Japan was still resisting. The test explosion in New Mexico was the dress rehearsal for the first use of atomic energy against human beings.

The Nazis and the Bomb

We may well wonder what the course of history would have been if Germany had been the first country to possess—and use—the atom bomb. What happened? After all, uranium fission was discovered in Germany, and the German scientists and technicians would have been capable of producing the bomb. And Hitler was most anxious to have a war-winning secret weapon. What went wrong?

When Professor Hahn published a paper on his discoveries in January, 1939, only the physicists and chemists who read it understood its implications. Professor Werner Heisenberg, then head of the Kaiser Wilhelm Institute of Physics, has told that official interest in nuclear physics among the Nazi leaders was rather small before the outbreak of the war. But when they learnt, presumably through their spy net in America, that the US Government had placed great financial resources at the disposal of the atomic research workers, a special bureau for co-ordinating similar efforts in Germany was set up and Professor Hahn and many other scientists were told that they were now under military orders. That was late in September, 1939.

According to Heisenberg, the scientists and their political superiors discussed, at their first meetings, the way in which the problem might be tackled. One possibility was to attempt the separation of the uranium isotope, the unstable U-235, from ordinary U-238, in order to get an atomic explosive; or, U-238 might be mixed with some matter that would slow down the neutrons without absorbing them, thus making a chain reaction possible. Ordinary water was unsuitable for that purpose, but heavy water, D_2O, was regarded as the ideal medium: water which consists of a 'heavy' isotope of hydrogen, called deuterium, with an extra neutron in its nucleus, and ordinary oxygen.

But where could they get heavy water in sufficient quantities? Facilities for its production were available at the Norsk Hydro works near Rjukan, in Norway; and there was also some heavy water in Paris, in Professor Joliot-Curie's laboratory.

In the dramatic days when the 'phoney' war ended, more than one scientist turned himself into a secret agent; the savant in his ivory tower, who believed he could keep out of the way of statesmen and generals and let the world go by, was a character of the past. When the Germans marched into Paris, two French scientists smuggled France's whole stock of heavy water, 165 litres, out of the country and brought it to England. But the Germans had also invaded Denmark, where they sought the co-operation of Professor Niels Bohr, promising him anything he might ask for in return for his help with their atomic research. To their surprise, Bohr accepted. First, of course, he asked them to let him know exactly how far they had got with their project.

The Nazis fell into the trap. Professor Bohr received all the information he required; he learnt about their plans to speed up heavy water production at Rjukan, now that the Germans were also the masters of Norway. Bohr passed this information secretly on to London, and continued to act as an Allied agent until things became too hot for him. In 1943 he escaped to Sweden in a fishing-smack, and a special Mosquito aircraft brought him to England.

One of the men who read Bohr's reports in London was Professor Leif Tronstad, formerly of Oslo University, who had been in charge of the Rjukan heavy water experiments.

30

He had fled to England after burning all his scientific papers. Appointed major in the Norwegian Army of Liberation, he devised a daring plan to put Rjukan out of action to deny its use to the Germans.

A Norwegian commando unit was set up and trained in Scotland under Tronstad's direction. In November, 1942, four of his men parachuted on to the Hardanger Plateau, installed themselves with their radio equipment in the mountains above Rjukan, and prepared the ground for the main force, which was to be brought over in two Halifax bombers, each towing a glider.

The first attempt failed: a gale compelled one of the bombers to turn back, and the other made a crash landing. The Germans rounded the survivors up and shot them. Immediately afterwards 6000 Gestapo-trained special troops were sent to the Rjukan area to protect the works from further Allied attacks.

But the Norwegians refused to give up. Six men of Tronstad's commando unit were parachuted into the Hardanger area, but they were erroneously dropped 25 miles from where the original party of four were still holding out. It took them a week to find the four men. One dark night in February, 1943, they all set out towards the Norsk Hydro plant, following Tronstad's carefully devised instructions.

Six men crept, one by one, through a narrow tunnel by which the high-tension cables enter the buildings, while the others covered the tunnel entrance, their tommy guns at the ready. On the shelves in the laboratory the commandos found ten large containers full of heavy water. They attached time-bombs to the shelves, and crawled back. The bombs went off after they had reached the safety of their hideouts. Germany's heavy water stocks had gone.

Speer's Fateful Decision

The Germans repaired the damage, and started afresh. In October, 1943, the RAF was called upon to bomb Rjukan. The machinery for producing heavy water was destroyed, but the Germans installed new equipment. By April, 1944, another stock of the precious liquid stood on the shelves, but the Nazi leaders wanted to prevent a further attack and decided to remove the whole lot to Germany.

British secret agents reported that the heavy water was to be ferried across Lake Tinsjoe before being transferred to railway trucks. It was clear that the transport would be strongly guarded, and a direct attack was out of the question. So Professor Tronstad devised an ingenious plan. Three parachutists dropped a magnetic mine in the lake. It exploded as the ferry passed over it. The secret battle of Rjukan was over.

Perhaps all these courageous and costly efforts to deprive the Germans of their heavy water were not really necessary. Only after the end of the war did the Allies hear of a momentous decision which had been reached in the leading Nazi circles.

Already in 1941 Heisenberg and another physicist had succeeded in operating a small pilot plant, a pile running on uranium and heavy water, at the University of Leipzig. By February, 1942, they were able to inform the Nazi leaders that 'a technical exploitation of atomic energy was definitely possible'. They were, however, thinking more on the lines of peaceful industrial uses, and Professor Hahn had told some of his colleagues early in the war, "If Hitler gets an atomic bomb, I shall kill myself." But as soon as the Nazi leaders heard of Heisenberg's success in Leipzig they placed the pile under the Military Research Council, which ordered the scientists to produce enough fissionable material for an atomic bomb.

In June, 1942, the Reichs Minister for Munitions, Speer, requested detailed information on the experiments. "Until then," reports Professor Heisenberg, "it had been merely a scientific problem. The question was whether atomic energy could be utilized at all. In Germany as well as in America, scientists had been working on similar lines, and arrived at nearly similar results at about the same time; now the decision had to be reached what technical consequences were to be drawn from them. But that decision was to be different in the two countries."

Speer made it. Atomic research was to continue merely on a limited scale. He did not believe in the atom bomb as a secret weapon, and time was short for new arms projects. Perhaps submarines and other ships could be driven by some atomic motor, said the Minister. From that day, says Professor Heisenberg, Germany devoted about one thousandth of the money and energy which the Americans invested in the atom bomb, to their own 'atomic-motor' project. Why did Speer and his advisers decide to drop the plan to produce the bomb? Germany's precarious military and economic situation, her limited resources, increasing Allied air attacks are only part of the answer. "The psychological attitude among the German leaders," says Heisenberg, "was the most important factor. They were still, even at that time, determined to force a quick decision on the battlefield, and expected to win the war in this way. A major enterprise such as the production of the atom bomb would have meant the long-term investment of much of the national effort in a weapon which could not be used soon. In order to be given the necessary facilities the German scientists would have had to make promises which they could not have kept. The German physicists aimed right from the start at keeping the scheme under their control, and used their expert advice towards securing the continuation of the work in the way which was eventually decided upon." In other words: those German scientists who, like Professor Otto Hahn, were determined not to let Hitler have that powerful weapon did not have to commit actual sabotage; all they had to do was to describe to the Nazi leaders the tremendous difficulties of the project, and advise them to drop it.

Still, if Hitler had taken a fancy to the atom bomb, things would have looked different. But it was he who believed in a 'quick decision on the battlefield'. He favoured the 'V' weapons, which were comparatively easy to make and could be used within a matter of months. Curiously enough, the only Nazi minister who believed in the possibilities of the atom bomb was the Postmaster-General. There is a record of a meeting he had with Hitler on the subject. But the Führer cut him short arrogantly: "Here I am, racking my brains how to win the war—and now the Postmaster-General, of all people, is going to tell me how!"

In February, 1944, an Allied air-raid destroyed part of the Kaiser Wilhelm Institute in Berlin. The Physics Department was moved to Hechingen in Württemberg, and the Leipzig pilot plant was installed nearby in a natural cave at Haigerloch, a small village. In February, 1945, the little reactor began to operate. Goering assumed control of the project, and made plans to evacuate the plant and the scientists to some inaccessible mountain retreat in the Bavarian Alps. In April, on the day after Hitler's last birthday, the first American troops entered the cave, and a special task force captured the research workers, including Hahn and Heisenberg. They were taken to a country house near Cambridge for a short spell of comfortable internment.

It was there that Hahn collapsed in despair when he heard that the first atom bomb had been dropped; he felt that his discovery of atomic fission had made him a guilty man. He was still interned when he was awarded the Nobel Prize for the same discovery.

The Manhattan Project

In the same month in which Speer decided to drop the atom bomb scheme, Churchill and Roosevelt started the 'Manhattan Project', the code name for the Allied drive to produce that new weapon. Until that time there had been no concerted effort, only a variety of advances and achievements by individual scientists and small teams.

The first, rather crude, atomic pile, or reactor, was built on the football ground of the University of Chicago by Enrico Fermi and his team. He scattered rods of natural uranium through a stack of graphite blocks; these acted as the 'moderator' for slowing down the neutrons emitted by fission. Fermi also inserted some rods of cadmium in his pile; this metal absorbs neutrons very readily, and the rods could therefore be used to control the chain reaction: when it expanded too much he pushed the cadmium rods in so that the fission process slowed down.

During the following two years the best nuclear physicists of the Western world, under the scientific leadership of the American, Professor Robert Oppenheimer, were cloistered in the vast research compound of Los Alamos, in the desert of New Mexico. Two thousand million dollars had been put aside for the Manhattan Project. Security precautions were more stringent than they had ever been in any prison. Yet the cooped-up scientists at Los Alamos could not be prevented from discussing the moral problems connected with the job they had in hand. There were passionate polemics about the rights and wrongs of what they were doing; most of those who had pangs of conscience, however, hoped that the war would come to an end before the bomb was ready.

After Nazi Germany's capitulation in May, 1945, that 'movement' among the scientists of Los Alamos grew in strength; they reminded each other that the Manhattan Project had been started only because there was the danger that Hitler might get such an all-powerful weapon, and perhaps win the war with it. Now that he was dead and gone there was no necessity to complete its development, let alone use it. Some of the leading nuclear physicists in America wrote memoranda and reports on these lines, and submitted them to President Roosevelt; but he died before reaching a decision—had he lived it might well have been that further work on the bomb would have been stopped.

Without Roosevelt's intervention, the vast machinery of the project was bound to be carried away by its own momentum. The test explosion of July 16th, 1945, was a complete success. Again the opposition among the scientists submitted a suggestion to the authorities: that Japan should be first warned of the existence of the bomb, and a demonstration of its devastating power given in some uninhabited area. The authorities refused to alter their plans; two atom bombs were to be dropped on Japan to compel her to surrender.

In the light of these early arguments between the American Government and the men who had created the most horrible weapon of all times, and who now felt scruples of conscience, much of the later controversies between the US Administration and the scientists becomes understandable. The military leaders were only interested in results; they were not interested in weighing the rights or wrongs of the matter, and intellectual qualms of conscience such as those felt by the scientists were alien to them. The road to Hiroshima and Nagasaki was free.

What were the mechanics of the atom bomb?

Professor Joliot-Curie has given a simple recipe of 'How to Make an Atom Bomb'. Take 60 lb of uranium 235, he said, and shape it into a hemisphere. Take the same amount again and shape it into a second hemisphere. Fix one half sphere at the end of a cylindrical tube, and place the mobile second half at the other. Spray some neutrons on the flat surface of the stationary hemisphere. Then shoot the second half against the latter so that you have a complete sphere of 120 lb, and drop the bomb quickly, because it is now about to explode.

In practice, however, things are a little more complicated. If you want a piece of uranium 235, the unstable isotope, to start a chain reaction it must be big enough; the technical term is 'critical size'. A minimum of 20 lb is believed to be the 'critical size' for U-235—in fact, this is still an anxiously guarded military secret. If the piece is too small then the majority of the neutrons which are constantly released in the uranium escape into the surrounding air; only if it is bigger than the 'critical size' will the neutrons find enough nuclei to start a chain reaction, and presently the entire lump of U-235 will explode.

Therefore the scientists adopted the device of cutting the 'critical size' in half and keeping the two halves apart until the moment the bomb was over the target. It had the shape of a huge aerial torpedo weighing 9000 lb and with an overall length of 25 ft. It contained a long cylinder lined with lead to protect the crew handling the bomb. The two hemispheres of U-235 were secured at either end of the cylinder; a time-fuse was used to operate a mechanism by which the upper half was 'shot' towards the lower one, thus giving the uranium charge its 'critical size'.

One of the major 'improvements' in atom bombs since Hiroshima has been the use of plutonium instead of U-235. To separate U-235 from U-238 is a difficult and costly process; the plant at Oak Ridge, Tennessee, which produced the U-235 for the first atom bombs employed 75,000 people in a vast complex of buildings dotted over 70 square miles—with a maximum output of only $6\frac{1}{2}$ lb of U-235 per day. To make 1 lb of it, 140 lb of U-238 were needed; as the two types of uranium cannot be separated in a chemical bath, the principal method used was to pump gasified uranium and fluorine through hundreds of fine filters. As the U-235 is lighter than the U-238, the two kinds of atoms can be caught in separate containers.

Plutonium, however, can be produced in a chemical separation plant. When an atom of U-238 is hit by a neutron travelling at medium speed it does not split, but absorbs the neutron; then, however, two electrons shoot out from the atom, and what remains is the atom of a new substance— plutonium, atomic number 94, atomic weight 239. After the bombardment of a mass of U-238, the plutonium can be extracted in a chemical bath. Today the main source of plutonium in America is the plant at Hanford, Washington State, while Britain makes her own plutonium at Windscale, and Calder Hall. In these plants U-235 neutrons are slowed down by blocks of graphite (pencil lead) before hitting U-238 atoms, which are thereby converted into plutonium. From time to time the uranium slugs are extracted and processed in chemical baths. The 'pile' in which the conversion takes place has to be shielded with concrete (some piles are also set deep in the ground) because the concentration of neutrons would be lethal to human beings.

Hiroshima and Nagasaki

While on Monday, August 6th, 1945, cheerful crowds in England enjoyed the first Bank Holiday after the end of the European war, an American aircraft dropped one bomb on the Japanese town of Hiroshima. It exploded 1000 ft above the ground just as the 255,000 people of the city were starting on their daily jobs.

Within the fraction of a second the U-235 in the bomb changed from a metal sphere into an immense mass of expanding gas, millions of degrees hot. The air itself around it began to burn. A shower of penetrating gamma rays attacked every living and dead object in the town. High-speed fragments of the uranium atoms shot in every direction. Then followed a shock-wave which shattered the buildings, and a tremendous blast of hot air whirled the debris of stone, metal, and wood over the ground. The bomb had the power of 20,000 tons of TNT.

92,133 people died either at once or after days and weeks of terrible suffering. More than 100,000 were permanently injured and disfigured. Within a half-mile radius around the main crater, which formed when the bomb exploded above, only one out of every ten people survived; within an area of three square miles only three out of every ten survived. The entire centre of the city was vaporized.

'Hiroshima does not look like a bombed city,' reported the first Allied newspaperman to see the town after Japan's surrender. 'It looks as if a monster steamroller had passed over it. All the atomic bomb left of dozens of blocks of city streets, houses, factories, and human beings, was three miles of reddish rubble.'

Our imagination is incapable of visualizing the apocalyptic terror which killed or maimed nearly 200,000 people, and eye-witnesses can only describe what they experienced on a very narrow sector. But some of these reports speak volumes. 'To distinguish the living from the dead was not easy,' writes the American journalist, John Hersey, in his famous account of what he heard from survivors, 'for most of the people lay still, with their eyes open. To Father Kleinsorge, an Occidental, the silence in the grove by the river, where hundreds of gruesomely wounded suffered together, was one of the most dread-

37

ful and awesome phenomena of his whole experience. The hurt ones were quiet; no one wept, much less screamed in pain; no one complained; none of the many who died did so noisily; not even the children cried; very few people even spoke. And when Father Kleinsorge gave water to some whose faces had been almost blotted out by flash burns, they took their share and then raised themselves a little and bowed to him, in thanks.'

Not even the children cried. . . . But they saw and suffered. Shuzo Nishio, a boy in his early teens, wrote this a few days after the explosion:

> The morning dawned. The fire was extinguished. We went down into the city from the hill. Wherever I looked there were the dead. Dead people with greatly swollen blisters; dead people from whose eyes an oily, sticky fluid was oozing. I was terribly frightened.
>
> There were many people I knew among the dead. The town was burnt to ashes. We waded through the ashes; they were still quite hot, and a nauseating smell came from them. We closed our noses. Where our house had been I only saw blackened walls, charred beams, and white ashes. I could not find my brother and my sister, only ashes. Only yesterday we were all together, now they have been turned into these ashes. I am sitting in the ashes. My tears are falling into them. Where my tears have dropped there are little black holes, many, many little black holes.

Three days later yet another atom bomb was dropped on Japan. It exploded at ground level in the town of Nagasaki, which had as many inhabitants as Hiroshima. 39,000 people were killed, 25,000 injured. One and a half square miles of the town were totally destroyed, and the whole was affected by blast. There was a tower of smoke and flame visible 250 miles away, forming a whirling dark grey cloud of that peculiar mushroom shape which we have come to associate with atomic explosions. Terrible heat-ray ripples followed the blast, and a rain of black particles fell upon the stricken city. 'The gigantic Mitsubishi steel works, hundreds of yards long, looked like a child's Meccano set that someone had trodden on,' reported a newspaperman. 'On the hill nearby, where once was one of the most up-to-date hospitals in the Far East, there was a sagging shell with bones lying in the ashes. No one came out of that hospital alive.'

In both towns all pregnant women within 1000 yd of the centre of the damage had subsequent miscarriages if they survived, and those within a radius of $1\frac{1}{4}$ miles gave birth to dead children. There was absolutely no protection against the gamma rays, not even in substantial buildings; the rays had the effect of passing through the skin, in many cases without seeming at first to affect it, but the blisters appeared within a few hours, and many victims died in terrible pain after a few days.

In the Nagasaki bomb, plutonium was used instead of U-235. Technically, it was not as effective as the Hiroshima bomb because it failed to explode at the required height of 1000 ft.

The Moral Shock-wave

The mushroom clouds had hardly drifted away from Hiroshima and Nagasaki when a shock-wave of horror and distress hit every nation on earth, victors, vanquished, and noncombatants alike. The prevailing mood was one of collective guilt, and there was widespread conviction that the new weapon would make an end of all wars. The international organization of Protestant Churches voiced these thoughts in a resolution which said that any nation which called itself Christian, yet was morally capable of using atomic energy in this way, was preparing the stage for the final destruction of mankind. The author of that resolution was an American politician by the name of John Foster Dulles. An American newspaper printed these sarcastic lines:

> The atom bomb is here to stay,
>   Most scientists agree.
> Oh, yes, the bomb is here to stay.
>   The question is, are we?

That question has forced itself with increasing intensity on everybody since 1945. If there was a moment when 'the ultimate weapon', the 'weapon to end all wars' might have been used for exactly that purpose, we let it pass. The military brains again took over from the conscientious minds, and treated the nuclear bomb exactly as new arms have been treated throughout human history: those who had them tried to keep them as a monopoly, and those who did not tried to get them. Better and bigger nuclear weapons were invented, built, and tested until an even more 'ultimate' weapon was created, the hydrogen bomb.

Future historians—if there *is* a future, and if history as we know it continues—will probably call our period mankind's saddest and maddest, and certainly the most dangerous. Human skill and ingenuity have harnessed the basic and most powerful forces of the universe, but we are giving priority to their use for destruction; we vote for the statesmen who conduct that policy, and we finance it with our tax money. We have a number of reasons for doing it, but the fact remains that we are making, storing, and testing arms not, as throughout history, to destroy a potential enemy, but to be able to devastate a substantial part of the earth completely, in the certain knowledge that our own part will be made uninhabitable just as thoroughly by the enemy. Besides, in any nuclear 'global war', as the military have termed this catastrophe, the resulting radiation from the explosion of all kinds of 'nuclear devices'—another favourite military term—is bound to affect all living organisms. What we are preparing, therefore, is simply the suicide of mankind. Current reasoning among those who favour this course is that war can be avoided only if both opponents are equally well armed with nuclear weapons. It is, of course, at best a gamble which may come off; on the other hand, judging by old-fashioned arms races which have inevitably led to war, it may not.

The testing of nuclear weapons, and the controversies it created, have been going on ever since the first atomic explosion in July, 1945. A year later the first 'nuclear manoeuvres' were held near the coral atoll of Bikini, in the South Pacific, where the US Navy staged its 'Operation Crossroads'. It was a series of tests of atom bombs against warships. A guinea-pig fleet of Japanese, German, and American vessels, most of them obsolete and ripe for the scrapheap, were anchored in the lagoon. Over 4000 animals—rats, goats, pigs, and so on, some in protective clothing and others smeared with anti-radiation ointment—were left on board.

A plutonium bomb was dropped from 30,000 ft; it exploded at a height of 400 ft above the ships. Five of them were sunk, two damaged beyond repair, and seven others suffered reparable damage. An enormous ball of fire enveloped the entire fleet, and an intense shower of gamma rays sprayed them. These rays alone would have killed most of the 30,000 men who would have made up the crew under normal conditions. Most of the animals were found burnt to death, or had to be killed because of their injuries.

Another atom bomb was exploded at Bikini three weeks later; it was suspended in a large water-tight tank a few fathoms below the surface. Those ships which had survived the first test were anchored in the vicinity. The bomb was exploded by radio-impulses from a distant ship. It threw ten million tons of water into the air. Two battle-ships and an aircraft-carrier sank, and a deluge of radio-active water engulfed the other ships.

Yet the days of the first Bikini series of tests seem almost idyllic when compared with the development which began in August, 1949. It was then that the first plutonium bomb was exploded in Russia. The monopoly of the Western Allies—to be more precise: of America—was gone, and the great nuclear arms race started.

The H-Bomb

Five months after Russia's first atom-bomb test President Truman gave the green light to his military advisers who clamoured for an even more powerful weapon than the nuclear fission bomb to overtake the Soviets again. Professor Oppenheimer, who had been responsible for the scientific side of the 'Manhattan Project', shrank back from this utter horror weapon. For a while he conducted a one-man campaign against those who wanted to force him into the new job. He was replaced by a more robust scientist without conscience troubles, confined to theoretical work, and eventually dropped altogether from secret work as a 'security risk'.

Already in the autumn of 1952 some preparatory experiments were carried out on the small island of Eniwetok in the centre of the Pacific, but the outside world was told next to nothing. It was all the more amazed, therefore, when in the summer of 1953 Stalin's successor, Malenkov, announced that the Soviet Union had the so-called hydrogen bomb. Was it true, or was it merely propaganda? A week later the seismographs of the Western world recorded a powerful explosion in the area of Wrangel Island, in the Arctic Ocean.

The implications were obvious. The Russians were in possession of a transportable, 'dry' hydrogen bomb; the American device at Eniwetok—it had been given the nickname of Lulu—had been in a much less developed stage: it was liquid and stationary, which meant that it was not yet a practical weapon. The Russians were clearly ahead in the nuclear race.

In March, 1954, however, America was again in the spotlight. Her first transportable H-bombs were successfully exploded at Bikini. One of them nearly 'ran away'—it proved to be much more powerful than the scientists had predicted. Reports and calculations on the new weapon made Hiroshima pale into insignificance. One such 'device', it was said, could reduce the major part of London or New York to ashes.

The excitement over the H-bomb reached its climax when the Japanese trawler *Lucky Dragon* returned from its fishing grounds 1000 miles from Bikini. The fishermen were dangerously ill from burns caused by radio-active dust—the 'fall-out' of the bomb. The fish they had caught were still radio-active. A panic seized all Japan, whose staple food is fish. And the world knew that from now on it would have to live under the cloud of the new bomb.

The H-bomb is not a fission device, but works by fusion, a process which we can see every time we lift up our eyes to the sun. The enormous energy which it radiates, and which makes life on our planet possible, results from a nuclear process which costs the sun about 5 million tons of mass every second (it has, however, enough for about another 30,000 million years). The nuclear process taking place in the sun is not the same as in the atomic fission bomb; in the sun, atoms are not split but fused: light atoms become heavier ones with a simultaneous loss of mass, which is converted into energy, into heat. In this process, hydrogen atoms 'fuse' to form helium atoms, which are nearly four times heavier: nearly, but not quite; when four protons—hydrogen nuclei—melt together into one helium nucleus, atomic weight 4, some mass is turned into energy, the heat that warms the earth.

How does Man produce fusion in the hydrogen bomb? Heavy hydrogen—deuterium, the hydrogen isotope which has one extra neutron in its nucleus, or tritium, which has two extra neutrons—is made to fuse at very great temperatures and to release its excess neutrons in a terrific flash of heat. (See Chapter VII.)

The technical difficulties of emulating on earth that process which has been going on in the sun for thousands of millions of years were quite formidable. When the American Government decided to make the hydrogen bomb it began by spending $1000 million on the construction of a plant for making tritium at Savannah River, South Carolina. The manufacture of this man-made hellfire became so costly that it became, in terms of capital investment, America's third-largest industry. We do not know what the Soviet Union spent on the enterprise; however, both projects were completed—one hesitates to use the conventional term 'successfully'—and the H-bomb has been with us ever since.

One of the greatest problems was the finding of a suitable 'fuse' for it, a device for producing the necessary high temperatures without which the 'melting' of the atoms cannot start. There was only one man-made device that could produce a temperature of some 100 million degrees F., and that was— the atom bomb. Therefore an 'ordinary' fission bomb was adapted as a fuse for the fusion bomb. Although that tremendous heat lasts for hardly more than one tenth of a millionth of a second, it is sufficient to start the breaking up of the tritium nuclei, with a devastating release of energy in the form of heat and blast, followed by sustained atomic radiation and great clouds of radio-active dust and ashes, travelling over as long a distance as the weather permits. The thermo-nuclear reaction is 'infectious'; it encroaches on the surrounding solid matter, on the air, on the water.

The fusion bomb has an immensely greater power of destruction than the fission bomb. Already 'Lulu' developed an energy of 3 megatons (3 million tons) of TNT explosive; its fireball enveloped an area of 5 miles—the zone of total destruction—within the space of four seconds, and its 'mushroom' measured 120 miles in width at a height of 25 miles, which it reached within ten minutes after detonation.

The runaway bomb of Bikini should have developed the same energy of 3 megatons, but in fact had 14; another H-bomb tested at Bikini developed 17 megatons, or the equivalent of 850 Hiroshima bombs. The radio-active calcium dust, the 'fall-out', which rained down on the unlucky *Lucky Dragon*, had the radio-activity of several hundred grams of pure radium.

There is some evidence that the Russian scientists have designed a new type of detonator for their H-bombs. A Japanese report on the fall-out after a series of Soviet test explosions in April, 1957, told of the discovery of 28 per cent of neptunium 239 in radio-active rain which pointed to the fact that the Russians were using this instead of U-235 or plutonium in their 'fuse' mechanism. Neptunium is a new artificial radio-active element which is produced when a neutron is absorbed by U-238; but neptunium 239 has a rather short life, half of its mass disintegrating every two to three days. The radio-active rain which fell over Japan must have travelled quickly from the test area, and one may assume that each megaton of the original explosion must have released about 10 kg of neptunium into the atmosphere. Calculations have shown that in every five atoms of uranium destroyed by fission at least one atom captures a neutron, thus turning it into neptunium. It may, therefore, be assumed that the Russian thermo-nuclear bomb consists of three parts: a primary detonator with a core of plutonium or U-235, a secondary detonator setting off the fusion process, and an outer sheath of U-238, which is the characteristic of what is termed a 'dirty' bomb—the type which scatters great masses of radio-active material into the atmosphere.

The thermo-nuclear bomb has been called the 'ultimate' weapon. But is it? Although the H-bomb and A-bomb stockpiles of America, Russia, and Britain may be more than sufficient to destroy organic life on earth to such an extent that mankind could no longer exist, Science can probably provide us with something even more effective: the cobalt bomb. It could destroy life on earth not in a flash but in a slow, inescapable process. A large thermo-nuclear bomb could be made with a casing of cobalt, which would capture the released neutrons; the explosion would turn it into a vast cloud of radio-active dust, which would not settle on the ground but travel around the earth for a long time, extinguishing organic life in its path. In the end only a few humans may be left over, and if they have retained the mental characteristics of our species they will then proceed to start the first post-nuclear war—with clubs.

The Geiger Counter

Radio-activity is invisible, inaudible, and impalpable—at least before its effects are felt. It can, however, be made visible and audible by means of an ingenious instrument, the Geiger counter; it derives its name from a German physicist,

Hans Geiger, who was one of Lord Rutherford's assistants and died in 1945.

The basic idea of the Geiger counter is simple. It consists of a glass cylinder filled with gas at a low pressure; two electrodes —one a metal tube, the other a fine wire stretched along its centre—are maintained at a large potential difference, usually about 1000 volts, but no spark will pass between them. Only when some subatomic particle enters the glass cylinder, where it will produce ionization (*ie*, the formation of electrically charged atoms), there is a sudden discharge between the two electrodes, and the potential drops for a fraction of a second. This is either registered on a voltmeter or made audible in a pair of headphones. Frequently, scientists attach to the Geiger tube a mechanical counting device such as a telephone counter as used by the Post Office to record the number of calls made by their subscribers; this registration of incoming particles can be made fully automatic by setting the telephone counter up beside a clock, and a photographic camera above it. The camera can be made to photograph the counter figures and the clock face automatically at regular intervals so that the research workers have a complete record on film of whatever radiation they are measuring.

On the other hand, some Geiger counters are made as small and light as possible so that they are portable. Apart from their use in research laboratories, Geiger counters have become indispensable in all plants using radio-active matter, in nuclear power stations, factories, for uranium prospecting, and, of course, in Civil Defence. The portable types are usually equipped with headphones. Trained workers can tell with their help if radiation exceeds the limit regarded as harmless to humans.

Radiation Hazards

But what *is* the maximum radiation which may still be regarded as harmless? That question, asked with increasing urgency during the last few years, may be of decisive importance to the human race even if nuclear war can be avoided.

The intensity of radiation is measured in units of 'roentgen', '*r*' for short. It is the amount of X- or gamma-radiation which will produce one unit of electricity in one cubic centimetre of air by ionization. To give a more tangible example: you need 600*r* to kill a man within a short time, and there is an inter-

45

national scientific agreement stating that $0.3r$ per week can be tolerated by humans without any danger to their health. On board the *Lucky Dragon* radiation from the fall-out of H-bomb ashes amounted to $0.1r$ per hour when the boat arrived back in Japan, *ie*, after seventeen days; the crew must have been subjected to altogether $400-600r$, and one of them died eight months later. According to the US Atomic Energy Commission, 7000 square miles received a dangerous dose of radiation; at a distance of 160 miles, where the fall-out began after eight hours, the radiation dose was $500r$ during the first thirty-six hours.

If the danger to human life and health through the testing of nuclear weapons were confined to the test area—some 1000 square miles of water in the Pacific, or of wasteland in Siberia or Australia—and if the fall-out immediately following the explosion were the only risk to organic life, there would not be much to worry about. However, there are much more sinister hazards, which have been explained by the world's leading scientists, and which have alarmed the public mind.

About 5 per cent of the matter released into the air at all kinds of nuclear explosions consists of radio-active strontium 90. It has a very long life, and is easily absorbed by organisms; as it sinks slowly down from the explosion cloud it may be carried anywhere by the wind. It poisons the water, the air, the soil, is absorbed by the grass and by vegetables, thus getting directly or indirectly—by way of cow's milk and animal meat—into the human body. There it accumulates in the bones, where it may produce cancer. As it has some chemical affinity to calcium, which is easily absorbed by growing children, strontium 90 is likely to cause more harm to them than to adults.

In November, 1957, a report published by four members of the United Kingdom Atomic Energy Authority at Harwell gave the results of some recent analyses for radio-active strontium, carried out on two English children who died in the summer of that year. Their bones were found to contain nearly a quarter of the strontium concentration above which, according to the Medical Research Council, 'immediate consideration would be required'. These were the highest concentrations ever found in the bones of people who had been nowhere near an atomic explosion. The strontium must have wandered around half the globe, and got into the milk which these children drank. Analyses have shown that the concentration of strontium in English milk rose by 250 per cent in the spring of 1955, a year after the Bikini tests, and remained at that level, which is, in itself, not dangerous; but strontium 90 accumulates in the body over the years.

In January, 1958, a Harwell health physicist told a group of European public-health specialists who attended a course on radiation hazards at Oxford that the fall-out from hydrogen-bomb tests nearly all comes down in a belt of temperate latitudes in the northern hemisphere embracing Britain, the European Continent including Russia, and North America. Strontium and cæsium, he said, were the only types of fall-out which might carry any serious hazards as they are taken up by the body from food; strontium was 'the real dark horse' —it had been falling steadily to earth over the last seven years and would go on doing so at the same rate for some years even if there were no more bomb tests.

According to some independent research groups in America, the amount of strontium in the bones of the US population will reach by 1970 the level at which 'immediate consideration' would be called for—even if no more test explosions are carried out! The UK Atomic Energy Authority has stated that the strontium 90 level in Britain has grown by 2·3 units per year since 1954, exceeding 10 units by mid-1958. The present annual rate of 20,000 deaths from leucæmia and bone cancer is therefore bound to rise.

There are many scientists who point to another danger, that from carbon 14, also a product of fission and fusion tests. This, too, is a radio-active isotope which wanders from the air to the ground and into the human body. It is the source of gamma radiations which can harm the 'genes', the physiological units of heredity which determine the characteristics in the offspring. Mutations caused in the genes by radiation may produce malformations and monstrosities; these mutations in any organic species nearly always occur towards the worse. Some doctors have already pointed out that births of defective children are increasing.

'Each nuclear bomb test spreads an added burden of radio-active elements over every part of the world,' said a petition signed by more than 9000 scientists from 44 countries, presented to the United Nations by Dr Linus Pauling, the American Nobel Prize winner, early in 1958. 'Each added amount of radiation causes damage to the health of human beings and to the pool of human germ plasm such as to lead to an increase in the number of seriously defective children that will be born in future generations.' The petition urged an international agreement to stop the testing of nuclear bombs at once.

The latter danger, the radiation hazards for future generations, has caused a great deal of discussion and speculation among the scientists as well as the general public. The truth is that we know little about it. Carbon-14 has a half-life of 5600 years, and during its long activity in organic matter it may change its host thousands of times. Neither biologists nor roentgenologists are yet prepared to state definitely what quantity of C-14 may be required to cause a mutation process; this quantity would have to act on the individual during the latter's 'reproductive life'. Experiments carried out on animals and insects with short reproductive lives, eg the fruit fly, have shown that mutations can be caused very easily, but we know next to nothing about the radiation 'tolerance' of humans or about the precise effects which are caused by a sub-atomic attack on the genes—except that they are extremely undesirable. On the other hand, one point on which most research workers agree is that there is no 'lower limit' below which any damage is impossible. Gamma rays are, of course, also active in X-ray diagnosis and treatment, and one result of the discussion on genetic hazards has been that doctors are now more careful with their X-ray applications.

Altogether, no less than thirty-three radio-active elements and 200 isotopes are produced in any thermo-nuclear explosion; their half-lives range from fractions of a second to thousands of years, but the most dangerous ones, like strontium 90, cobalt 60, and cæsium 137, all of them beta and gamma radiators, have half-lives of from 25 to 275 years. Besides, a thermo-nuclear explosion causes the 'combustion' of the nitrogen in the air into nitric oxide (a 20-megaton explosion may produce 500,000 tons of it), which combines with the water vapour in the atmosphere to form nitric acid; this has a destructive effect on plant life when descending mixed with rain.

Efforts to produce what is called a 'clean' bomb, with a minimum of fall-out, can be successful within certain limits; but any atomic explosion has such a great variety of harmful effects that the damage to organic life, present and future, can never be confined to some restricted area. Those responsible for the nuclear arms race are, of course, trying to reassure us that the danger is negligible. However, all these assurances sound unconvincing if one reads such publications as the handbook published in July, 1957, by the US Atomic Energy Commission; it deals, among other things, with radiological warfare:

> For some time consideration has been given to the possibility of using radio-active material deliberately as an offensive weapon. . . . The basic idea is that radio-active contamination of areas, factories, or equipment would make their use either impossible or very hazardous. . . .

The practical execution of this kind of warfare is still a military secret, but we may be sure that preparations are well advanced on both sides of the Iron Curtain. From the atomic shell to be used in open combat to the inter-continental ballistic missile with an H-bomb warhead, the arsenal of a future nuclear war seems to be well stocked, and what we are now getting in the way of test hazards is already some foretaste of the holocaust to come in the event of a new war. Many leading scientists—among them Otto Hahn, Albert Schweitzer, Professor Joliot-Curie, and Bertrand Russell—have issued very emphatic warnings to stop the nuclear arms race and the bomb tests. "It is wrong to leave it to the politicians," said Professor Marcus Oliphant, the Australian atomic scientist, in 1957. "A lot of the time they do not know what they are up to."

Thus it is understandable that in this matter of life and death the ordinary people are trying to make their voices heard above those of the politicians and generals, and to enforce the exclusive use of atomic power for the purposes of peace. If all the money, the resources, the effort, and the manpower which are at present employed in preparing the suicide of the human race were devoted to raising the standard of living all over the earth, the results might well be staggering. "If you succeed in using the nuclear-physical findings for peaceful purposes," said Albert Einstein, "it would open the way to a new paradise."

III

THE REACTOR FAMILY

IT IS a sad thought that so many of mankind's greatest inventions have been used first as weapons. The Chinese are, perhaps, the exception among the nations of the earth—they never used the gunpowder which they had invented to kill their enemies, but to make fireworks. In the Western world, however, the tradition has been to make swords first and ploughshares later.

In the case of atomic energy there were special reasons for this. The fear that Germany would make great efforts to produce an atom bomb spurred the Allies to combine their scientific and technological knowledge and resources towards the same goal. Besides, the uncontrolled chain reaction of a 'critical mass' of fissionable material is much more easy to achieve than the controlled one, which alone can produce energy for the homes and factories, for transport and research.

What, then, is the essential difference between controlled and uncontrolled chain reaction?

Let us return to the football ground of Chicago University where Enrico Fermi built the first nuclear reactor in December, 1942 (it has been rebuilt in the Argonne National Laboratory near Chicago). The term 'reactor' did not yet exist; Fermi called his contraption of uranium rods and graphite blocks a 'pile'—the name came to his mind because this was, like the Voltaic pile, an energy-producing battery. Fermi used natural uranium, ie a mixture of about 140 parts of the stable U-238 to one part of the unstable isotope, U-235. We know that when a neutron hits the nucleus of a U-235 atom the nucleus may split, releasing a few neutrons, which in their turn will hit other nuclei and split them. This chain reaction is common to the atom bomb as well as to the reactor. In the bomb it 'goes mad', as a Harwell scientist has called it very aptly; in the reactor we can control it.

The fission product in which we are most interested if we want to generate power is heat. As the two parts of the split nucleus fly apart with high velocity, the energy of movement of these fission fragments is converted into heat by braking collisions with neighbouring atoms; or, simply, matter is converted into heat. In order to produce the warmth of a one-kilowatt electric fire, more than 30 million million fissions per second are necessary!

One may ask what makes the production of heat in the atom so different from that when coal is being burnt or petrol vapour exploded. The answer is that in ordinary combustion there is merely a chemical change; atoms alter their combinations with other atoms, forming new molecules—but their nuclei remain untouched and unchanged. For instance: in a coal fire one atom of carbon and two atoms of oxygen combine into a carbon dioxide gas molecule; the violent movement of molecules causes heat. The energy released from one atom of fissile material, however, is 50 million times as great as that produced by an atom in the combustion of hydrogen when petrol vapour explodes in the cylinder of a motor-car! Although we may believe that matter 'disappears' when coal is burnt or petrol exploded, this is not true; it changes into other matter, such as gas, but it is still there. In nuclear fission, however, matter actually vanishes completely to become energy according to Einstein's famous equation: $E = mc^2$. But *what* matter turns into energy? *Which* piece of the nucleus would be missing if we could put it together again after fission? We still do not know for certain, although a great deal of speculation has naturally been done by the physicists. Neither the protons nor the neutrons or electrons involved in the process disappear; they can usually be accounted for. Nor do they become smaller. So it must be some other matter in the nucleus that vanishes to become energy. Is it the mesons, the 'atomic glue'? Scientists also presume the existence of yet another sub-atomic particle, the neutrino, uncharged, like the neutron, but with very small mass, to sustain the law of 'conservation of mass and energy' in nuclear reactions: the law that the sum total of mass and energy is constant for any system and cannot increase or decrease—that neither mass nor energy can be created out of nothing or reduced to nothing.

Fermi was careful to prevent his 'pile' from 'going mad'. We know that he had to interlace his uranium rods with a 'moderator' from which the fast neutrons would bounce off, thus being slowed down, and therefore more likely to keep moving until they happen to strike a nucleus; fast neutrons—those ejected by the fission process travel at a speed of about 10,000 miles per second—are likely either to shoot out of the pile without hitting a nucleus, or to be 'swallowed up' by one, becoming inextricably attached to it. Fermi used graphite as a moderator; heavy water and even ordinary water may also be used for slowing down fast neutrons. But the moderator cannot be used to control the chain reaction at the same time; therefore, yet another 'foreign body' had to be introduced in the form of control rods, to be raised or lowered in the pile according to need.

For this purpose, Fermi used cadmium rods, but boron has since been found equally effective. Both elements absorb neutrons strongly; if the chain reaction threatens to become too fast it can be retarded by lowering the control rods into the pile. Neutrons will then be absorbed at such a rate that out of the two or three produced by each fission, less than one is left free to travel on through the pile.

Come-back of the Steam Turbine

If you want to use atomic energy for the production of power, you have to convert the heat which is created in the pile into some other form of energy which can be used in the homes and factories—that is, into electricity. There is an engine which is ideally suited as a link between the reactor and the electric generator: the good old steam turbine.

In a motor-car the heat given off by the engine is a waste product; it is carried off by water, made to circulate in the engine and cooled by the radiator. In a nuclear reactor which is used for the production of power the 'coolant' may be ordinary water, heavy water, some specially suitable gas, or even liquid metal; its function is to carry the heat out of the pile and make it available for the raising of high-pressure steam for the turbine, which drives the electric generator.

Theoretically, steam could be produced in the pile and then led directly into the turbine. But anything in contact with the pile is highly dangerous because it may have become radioactive; therefore, the 'coolant' is made to circulate in a closed circuit which contains a heat exchanger. Here the heat from the pile is transferred to ordinary water, which is thereby turned into steam. This prevents any contamination of the electricity-generating unit.

These, then, are the essential elements of the power-producing nuclear reactor: the 'fuel' (*eg* uranium rods); the 'moderator' (*eg* graphite); the 'control rods' (*eg* boron); and the 'coolant' (*eg* water, gas, or liquid metal). The installation comprises the heavily-shielded pile, the closed-circuit coolant ducts leading to the heat exchanger, the steam-turbine and, geared to it, the electric generator.

We may call this the 'conventional' design of a power-producing reactor. The atomic engineers regard it already as somewhat old-fashioned. They call it the slow reactor because

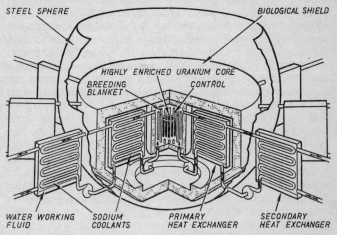

FIG. I The 'fast fission breeder' reactor which produces more atomic fuel than it consumes. This type is used at Dounreay, Scotland.

it works with neutrons whose speed is reduced by the moderator. It is not very economical; it uses up a great deal of the precious U-235, of which the world has only limited resources. True, it converts some of the not-so-precious U-238 into the radio-active element plutonium, which in its turn can be used as nuclear fuel like U-235 (at present, however, most of the plutonium produced in nuclear reactors goes into the making of atomic weapons). But on balance there is an appreciable loss of fuel.

Recent advances in nuclear engineering have made it possible to make a 'fast' reactor—and this type can produce more fissile material than it uses up. In the fast reactor the neutrons are not slowed down, but to make the chain reaction possible it is run almost exclusively on highly fissile material —'enriched' fuel, as it is called. In fact, a fast reactor is a form of atom bomb cleverly prevented from blowing up!

As this type of reactor uses hardly any U-238 as fuel it does not require a moderator for slowing up the neutrons, thus protecting them from being 'captured' by stable nuclei. But if the core of the pile is surrounded by an envelope of U-238 or thorium, the neutrons which do not take part in the chain reaction will produce a nuclear transformation—they help to 'breed' new nuclear fuel. Thorium is a mildly radio-active element which turns into the highly radio-active uranium isotope U-233. This, like plutonium, is an excellent reactor fuel. As the world has plenty of thorium, the 'fast-breeder' reactor is extremely economical: it produces, in fact, more nuclear fuel than it consumes! An experimental reactor using thorium for breeding in the blanket is also being constructed at the new research station at Winfrith Heath, Dorset.

A fast reactor using 'enriched' fuel can be made much smaller and more compact than a slow one; the size of the core can be reduced, and coolants which permit higher temperatures may be used. The absence of a moderator is another factor which simplifies design. For these reasons, the fast reactor —apart from its use as a breeder—can be made so compact that it appears suitable as a mobile power unit in transport at sea and eventually perhaps in the air.

Reactors to Measure

At the end of 1945, Britain initiated its own atomic-energy organization. It had to start almost from scratch because most of the technological and scientific 'know-how' from the Manhattan Project was being anxiously guarded by the American authorities, although British scientists had played a decisive part in carrying it through. A complete research and production organization had to be built up in Britain before any practical use could be made of nuclear energy; it was developed on two lines, a research branch centred on Harwell, a former airfield near Oxford, and a production branch, now called the Industrial Group, with its HQ in Risley, near Warrington, Lancashire, both operating under a special body, the United Kingdom Atomic Energy Authority.

The first reactors to be built in Britain were two research

piles, one called BEPO, an abbreviation of 'British Experimental Pile O', and GLEEP, 'Graphite Low Energy Experimental Pile'. Scientists have a weakness for homely-sounding abbreviations; DIMPLE (Deuterium Moderated Pile, Low Energy), ZEPHYR (Zero Energy Fast Fission Reactor), ZEUS, DIDO, LIDO, PLUTO and others were to follow.

BEPO and GLEEP, both working with uranium metal and uranium dioxide as fuel and with graphite as moderator, became the ancestors of the production reactors which are now serving quite a number of purposes. They provided the 'know-how' needed if Britain wanted to become Europe's leading 'atomic nation'. ZEPHYR and ZEUS, which began operation in 1954 and 1955 respectively, are fast breeder reactors using plutonium and U-235 as fuel; they have become the 'fathers' of the great 'golden ball', the spherical reactor of the atomic experimental station at Dounreay, Caithness. The research carried out at Harwell on graphite-moderated, gas-cooled reactors was the foundation on which the world's first commercial nuclear power station, Calder Hall, was built.

Within the short time since the end of the Second World War, reactors for all kinds of purposes have been developed, tested, and put into operation. The choice of fuel, moderator, and coolant depends on the use to which the pile will be put, and there is no point in asking which type is more efficient or economical. The first question which has to be settled in each case is that of size. This must be decided according to the fate which a newly-born neutron in the reactor may have to undergo. If we want to slow it down in the moderator to produce another fission, or if we want it to be 'captured' by a U-238 nucleus—the pile will have to be built accordingly. Perhaps we want it to escape altogether from the core; the bigger the core, the smaller is the chance of a neutron escaping from it. Here we are coming up against the vital problem of 'criticality'; the critical size is reached when the rate of escape of neutrons, added to their rate of capture, is just equal to the rate at which they are freed by fission. Only then can the chain reaction set in.

In contrast to all other 'prime movers', such as steam or petrol engines, the size of a reactor is, therefore, *not* determined by the required power output, but by 'criticality'. This is the first consideration when building a reactor to measure. The second is the permissible rate of heat release, which alone may limit the power output, and this in turn is a matter of engineering design. Thus the problem of fitting a reactor in, say, an airliner is not only one of weight and safety—a fact which answers the question why it takes the engineers such a long time to adapt nuclear energy for transport.

The most widely used reactor systems may be classified into six categories, all of them working with natural or enriched uranium, which permits the reduction of the core to a minimum:

Moderator	Coolant
Graphite	Gas
Graphite	Sodium
Ordinary water	Ordinary water
Heavy water	Ordinary water
Heavy water	Heavy water
Heavy water	Gas

Scientists and engineers can, therefore, ring the changes according to the special requirements of the reactor they are building. Besides the above-listed moderators they may also use beryllium, and we have already mentioned the possibility of using liquid metal as a coolant. When water is used for cooling, one of two systems may be employed: in the 'pressurized' system the water is kept at high pressure (up to 2000 lb per square inch); alternatively, it may be made to enter the core just below boiling point, and boil on its way through the pile, developing a high proportion of steam. Observing certain precautions to avoid radio-active contamination, this steam may be fed directly to the turbines, without using a heat exchanger.

A heavy-water moderated reactor, on the other hand, has another advantage: it can operate not only with enriched uranium but also with natural uranium as fuel. However, although natural uranium is cheap, heavy water is expensive; and the use of natural uranium requires a minimum size of about 13 ft for the reactor vessel.

Where gas is used as a coolant, the amount of heavy water for the moderator can be very much reduced. The Russians have built an interesting reactor of this type: the vessel is filled with heavy water in which the fuel rods, natural uranium in light metal tubes, are suspended. The coolant is carbon di-

56

oxide gas under pressure; it enters the pile at 90° C and leaves it at 420° C. A power station of this type may reach an output of more than 100,000 kw.

Britain's first nuclear power station, Calder Hall, which we shall describe in detail in the next chapter, uses natural uranium as fuel, graphite as moderator, and carbon-dioxide gas as coolant. The gas is heated in the core to a temperature of 350° C; it gives up its heat in the heat exchanger and re-enters the core at about 140° C. This is now considered the 'conventional' type of thermal reactor—relatively large, a little cumbersome, but safe and reliable. The Americans have built an experimental sodium-graphite reactor; it began to operate near Los Angeles in 1957. It is a slow-neutron reactor using slightly enriched uranium (2·8 per cent of U-235 in natural uranium), graphite as moderator, and liquid sodium as coolant. The use of this metal for heat transfer makes higher output of power possible without pressurization, as in the case of water or gas. Besides, as the boiling point of sodium is very high (882° C), there is no limitation of coolant temperature, apart from that imposed by the metal tubes and containers through which it is fed. However, sodium becomes easily radio-active and must therefore be well shielded; so must the graphite in the core because it readily absorbs neutrons, thus losing its value as a moderator after some time. But every type of reactor has its pros and cons.

Britain is experimenting with a new type of reactor at Winfrith Heath in Dorset. Its fuel consists of a mixture of uranium and carbon, the latter acting as a moderator. The two elements are combined in the form of a carbide, which has the physical properties of ceramics and does not melt at high temperatures. This reactor has the advantages of low initial and operating cost and high operating temperatures (up to 800° C). The main drawback is that the coolant gas will have a substantial amount of radio-activity when it emerges from the core.

Research at Dounreay

It is, of course, illogical to say that the Calder Hall reactor was already outdated at the time it began to operate; but liquid-metal-cooled thermal reactors may well be the next stage in power-station design. Beyond that, reactors with a much higher utilization of fuel will be required to satisfy the world's increasing energy requirements, and here the fast breeder seems to be a promising type.

The United Kingdom Atomic Energy Authority, therefore, decided to build a research and development centre to study the scientific and technical problems which have to be solved before a fast reactor can operate on an industrial or commercial scale: this is what the establishment at Dounreay, Caithness, Scotland, will be doing. Its two reactors became critical in 1958, and its 'golden ball', the spherical reactor vessel, has become the symbol of advanced nuclear research.

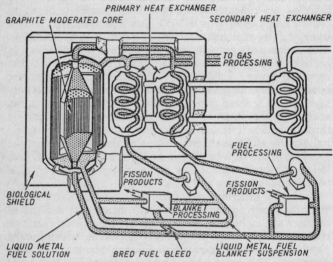

FIG. 2   The liquid-metal-fuelled reactor: a 'breeder' type in which enriched fuel is dissolved in a liquid metal carrier. It offers low fuel costs and cheap power.

In short, Dounreay will provide the operating experience necessary for building the reactors of future years, and collect information on the behaviour of fuel elements, cooling systems, and controls. Safe disposal of residues, the treatment and storage of radio-active effluents, and similar questions also form an important part of its task. It will also work as a power station, producing 15,000 kw for the national grid.

Dounreay is also a material-testing station like the PLUTO

and DIDO reactors at Harwell, and it fabricates fuel elements for the latter and for reactors abroad, using new and improved fuel materials. More fissile material will be formed in the breeding 'blanket' around the core than is used up in the reactor. The core uses enriched uranium 235 or plutonium; the breeder around it consists of about 2000 rods of natural uranium, each 8 ft long. This blanket reflects the neutrons back into the core as they try to escape, and fresh fissile material is generated in it. There is, of course, no moderator. The coolant, which is being pumped into the top of the reactor vessel, consists of liquid sodium-potassium; from this primary coolant the heat is transferred to a second coolant circuit in the heat exchangers (it has twenty-four of them), and eventually to water, which it turns into steam. This is fed into the turbo-alternators to generate electricity.

The 'golden ball' of Dounreay, which has been called the shape of things to come in atomic architecture, serves two purposes. This sphere of 135 ft diameter will localize the spread of fission products should they be accidently released from the reactor; and it can withstand any variations of pressure, which might occur as a result of a liquid-metal fire in the sphere. It is, in fact, one of the largest pressure vessels ever built.

Danger at Windscale

The sphere of Dounreay is, therefore, a design for safety as well as a landmark of the atomic age. The importance of the safety factor in the operation of nuclear establishments was brought home to the British public in October, 1957, when an accident occurred at the plutonium works at Windscale in Cumberland, a stone's throw from Calder Hall. The Windscale reactors are used for the production of tritium and plutonium, mainly for atom and hydrogen bombs, and of fission products such as cæsium and strontium, which are then processed at the Radiochemical Centre near Amersham, Buckinghamshire.

It was Britain's first serious atomic accident. One morning the maintenance men under the physicist in charge carried out a routine operation called 'roasting': the heating-up of the uranium core to release energy accumulated in the graphite moderator. This would have been perfectly all right if the 'roasting' had not been carried out too soon after a similar operation, without giving the reactor enough time to cool off. The result was that it became overheated, and that perhaps some lithium cartridges, which were also in the reactor at the time —they are used for the manufacture of tritium—caught fire.

In considering the cause of the accident, the official report of the investigation committee said that the phenomenon of the storage of energy in graphite through neutron bombardment —called 'Wigner energy' after its discoverer—had been known for some time, 'but when the Windscale pile was built knowledge was scanty. . . . Wigner energy can be released and eight such releases had been carried out by the end of 1956 in Pile No. 1. The pile is shut down, and the coolant air flow stopped, thus raising the uranium and graphite temperature and so starting the Wigner release in the graphite. The release is then self-sustaining. It has always been found difficult to release energy in all the graphite. Consequently, on three previous occasions, it was found necessary to apply a second nuclear heating.'

Because of badly placed registering-gear the rapid overheating of the core as a result of the second 'roasting' went at first unnoticed, and only late at night did the physicist in charge, who was watching the automatic thermometers, realize that the temperature was still rising when it should have dropped after the release of Wigner energy from the graphite. He ordered that the control rods be fully run in at once to cool the uranium. But the damage leading to the accident had already been done.

Throughout the following day the temperature kept rising. The uranium was, in fact, burning, or rather smouldering, and eventually the graphite caught fire also. One fuel cartridge after another burst. By the evening of the third day the fire was affecting about 150 fuel channels. A major fire was raging inside the reactor, and the Geiger counters were ticking away with increasing rapidity: radio-active matter was escaping through the filters at the top of the reactor.

Volunteers in protective suits went up in a hoist normally used for loading new fuel rods. They opened one of the plugs in the side of the furnace, and saw to their horror that the uranium rods were red-hot.

An attempt was made to squirt carbon dioxide into the pile. It failed. Eventually it was decided to use the time-honoured weapon against fire—water. Never before had water been poured on red-hot uranium, and no one knew for certain what would happen, except that the reactor would be wrecked. The police and fire brigade stood by for an emergency. The plugs were opened again and hoses stuck in. The staff, the police, and the firemen got under cover and put on their facemasks. Then the water was turned on.

At first there seemed to be no effect. About an hour later the auxiliary cooling fans, which had been kept in operation to maintain a minimum flow of air through the pile, were shut down to deprive the fire of fresh oxygen, and immediately the water began to have its effect. It was kept on for over twenty-four hours.

Late in the afternoon of the fifth day the pile was cold at last. Pile No. 1 was wrecked, a great deal of precious material and equipment ruined. But the danger of a catastrophe had been averted.

Outside the Windscale works there was considerable anxiety and excitement as more and more radio-active matter escaped from the chimney during those critical five days. In the milk of cows within a wide range around Windscale radio-active iodine was found at a concentration six times as high as the permissible life-time maximum; radio-iodine tends to accumulate in the thyroid glands, whose functioning it may disturb seriously, especially in young children. Therefore the distribution of milk from farms in the area had to be banned until radio-activity in the district returned to its normal level. The same measures had to be taken a few years earlier in Canada when one of the reactors at the Chalk River plant met with a similar accident.

As far away as London, radio-activity from Windscale was found to affect the atmosphere. The Kodak Company, which normally monitors the level of atmospheric radio-activity because an increase would affect the sensitive layers of photographic material, stated that, for an hour, there was an increase of about 6 per cent—comparable with increases registered after hydrogen-bomb tests in the Pacific and Siberia.

Although the quantity of radio-activity released was altogether considerably greater than at Hiroshima, nobody's health was seriously affected by the accident, but it might have been a different story if the fire had not been put out in time to prevent it from spreading to other parts of the plant. The White Paper containing the official report blamed 'certain weaknesses in organization' and 'certain gaps in our scientific knowledge' for the accident; the general impression, however, was that it was mainly due to insufficient experience of the maintenance staff and to faulty instruments: things, in short, which might easily cause some similar or even greater mishap at any atomic establishment and at any time. The question has been asked, therefore, whether the nuclear-power stations which will soon be dotted all over the civilized world might not increase the hazards of radio-activity even in an age of peace and security from nuclear tests.

The United Kingdom Atomic Energy Authority dealt with this question in an appendix to the White Paper. 'The air used for cooling at Windscale,' it said, 'can react with uranium at 350° C. The new reactors (*ie* those used in power stations) are cooled by carbon dioxide, which does not react with uranium until the temperature is greater than 650° C. The new reactors will use carbon dioxide circulating in a closed circuit for cooling so that there will be no discharge into the atmosphere. . . . The arrangements for detecting burst fuel elements are superior, and the instrumentation at the civil reactors is much improved.'

But the same accident rarely happens twice, and there may be many as yet unsuspected risks besides the Wigner release. Complacency about anything connected with so young a branch of technology as the utilisation of nuclear energy is bound to lead to new accidents. 'It must be clearly recognized,' said the *Manchester Guardian* leader writer, 'that it is impossible to build atomic reactors that run themselves like automatons. Somewhere there must be men who make decisions and who press buttons. It must be recognized that men can make mistakes which no automatic gear can prevent; and that the consequences of serious mistakes in the operation of atomic reactors can be serious indeed. So it is the men who in the end matter.'

A new tool will help them: a closed-circuit television camera specially designed to be lowered into nuclear reactors so that the engineers can carry out regular inspections from a safe distance. It is so slim that it can 'look around' inside a fuel channel only 4 in in diameter; it can withstand gamma radiation and temperatures up to 200° C.

The Harwell Story

A sleepy village on the Berkshire Downs, which had little connection with the outside world until the RAF built an airfield near it in 1939, was chosen as the site of Britain's great Atomic Energy Research Establishment after the Second World War. When the airmen moved out in January 1946, the builders moved in.

Since then Harwell has been the place where, in the short space of a dozen years, more creative scientific ideas were developed than perhaps anywhere else in the world. From the time when the first green-and-yellow prefabs were put up to house a nucleus of research workers under Professor—now Sir John—Cockcroft, until the present day, this vast maze of reactor houses, laboratories, machine plants, lecture rooms, and living quarters has contained a strange, intense life of its own behind the security fences which separate it from the hills and fields and villages around. Starting from scratch, the men and women of Harwell have succeeded in making Britain the cradle of many of the most advanced prototypes and techniques of the atomic age.

Harwell's research reactors have stood at the beginning of each new development. During the first twelve years, twelve reactors, each with its special task and design, were set up (see p. 64).

Each member of this family of reactors has its own distinct individuality, its history, its characteristics. DIDO, for example, is the most potent research reactor in Western Europe, with a power of 10,000 kw and an extremely high 'flux' of neutrons. PLUTO, also with a power of 10,000 kw, has six test 'loops', each of which provides a pilot model of the essentials of a future reactor system. DIDO and PLUTO also have facilities for producing radio-active isotopes, particularly radio-active cobalt 60; these two reactors produce the equivalent of no less than 50 gm of radium a year.

The old BEPO is constantly in use for about fifty experiments; this reactor, too, has 'loops': test arrangements containing fuel element samples around which circulates gas of the same kind and at the same temperature as that to be used in the final life-size reactor. The 'loops' are in operation for months; then the fuel element is removed in a highly radio-active state and examined behind thick lead walls by remote-handling gear.

The first reactors built for the Central Electricity Authority extract the heat equivalent of 10,000 tons of coal for each ton of uranium. This sounds a good achievement, but theoretically a breeder reactor could do a hundred times better by burning the abundant U-238 or thorium. The two 'zero energy' reactors, ZEUS and ZEPHYR, fuelled by U-235 and plutonium respectively, were built to work towards this more intensive utilization of nuclear fuel. Each of these reactors has

THE HARWELL REACTORS

NAME	PURPOSE	DATE OF START-UP	MODERATOR	COOLANT	FUEL
GLEEP	General reactor research; biological irradiation	1947	Graphite	Air	Natural uranium
BEPO	General radiation source; isotope production	1948	Graphite	Air	Natural uranium
ZEPHYR	Fast reactor and breeder research	1954	—	—[2]	Plutonium
DIMPLE	Thermal reactor (power production) research	1954	Heavy water	—[2]	Varied
ZEUS	Core design study for Dounreay fast reactor	1955	—	—[2]	Uranium 235
ZETR now superseded by:	Study of homogeneous reactor types[1]	1955	Heavy or natural water	—[2]	U-233, U-235, Plutonium
HAZEL	Basic nuclear research	1958	Heavy water	—[2]	Enriched U-238 dissolved in moderator
LIDO	Research into new types and shielding	1956	Natural water	Natural water	U-235
DIDO	Isotope production, neutron research, reactor fuel study	1956	Heavy water	Heavy water	U-235
NERO	Design research into advanced graphite-moderated power reactors	1957	Graphite	Sodium	Varied
PLUTO	Testing of fuel and component materials for power reactors; production of cobalt-60 for cancer treatment	1957	Heavy water	Heavy water	U-235
NEPTUNE	Development of submarine propulsion	1957	Natural water	—[2]	Enriched U-238

[1] Homogeneous reactors: see p. 66.
[2] These reactors operate at a very low power level so that they will not get highly radio-active and consequently do not require cooling.

a core of U-235 rods surrounded by a 'blanket' of natural uranium, in which the surplus neutrons from the core are captured, thus turning the blanket into plutonium; in ZEPHYR it was shown that for each fissile atom destroyed in the core, more than two new fissile atoms are produced in the blanket —the scientists call this a 'breeding gain factor' of over two.

ZEUS and ZEPHYR have supplied the technological know-how for the Dounreay fast breeder reactor, 'the nuclear physicist's dream', as Sir John Cockcroft has called it.

NERO derives its name from the description 'Na (chemical symbol for sodium) Experimental Reactor, Zero Energy (O)'. One of its main jobs is the design study of a sodium-cooled, graphite-moderated reactor, the type which might well play an

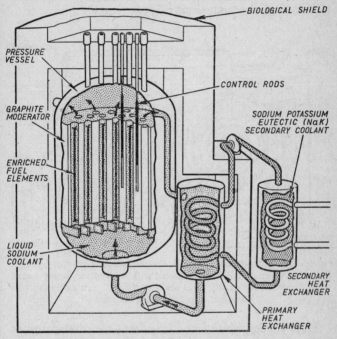

FIG. 3 The sodium-graphite reactor, a controversial type. Here the gas coolant of the Calder Hall type reactor is replaced by liquid sodium.

important part in nuclear power during the next few years. But Harwell looks beyond that second generation of reactors to even more advanced types. One of them aims at working at very much higher fuel temperatures than the first and second generation; for higher temperatures mean higher output and efficiency. This can be achieved by using fuel in a ceramic, uncanned form instead of a metallic one. In this system, fissile uranium 233 is burnt in the core and some of the neutrons released are captured in thorium to produce further supplies of U-233 by nuclear transmutation. The fissile and the 'fertile' materials and a moderator are to be combined in a nearly homogeneous system, and the heat developed will be transferred by gas under pressure. The advantages of this reactor type are high thermodynamic efficiency and low fuel costs.

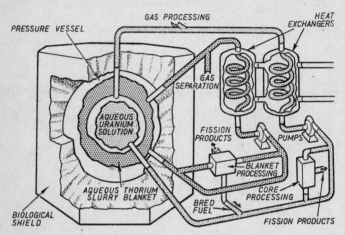

FIG. 4 The homogeneous aqueous reactor, which offers cheap power. Its fuel, a uranium sulphate, is mixed with the coolant, heavy water. It produces not only energy but also new fuel by turning its thorium 'blanket' into fissionable material.

These studies, which take a long time—the development of a new reactor type may take ten years or more—are mainly carried out with the help of HAZEL (Homogeneous Assembly —Zero Energy), which specializes in basic and homogeneous-reactor research. We call the 'conventional' pile heterogeneous because the fuel, the moderator, and the coolant are separate elements. In the homogeneous type the fuel and the moderator are combined into one mixture and sealed off in ceramic, and the scientists aim at mixing the coolant as well into that 'soup'. It may, for instance, consist of uranium sulphate dissolved in heavy water (the latter acting as moderator plus coolant), or of a liquid metal such as bismuth, in which the uranium fuel is suspended. The whole solution is pumped from the interior of the reactor to the heat exchanger, where it is cooled, and back again in a continuous flow. However, we may not see this advanced type of thermal reactor in operation before 1960 or thereabout but the scientists and technologists regard it as 'a great hope'.

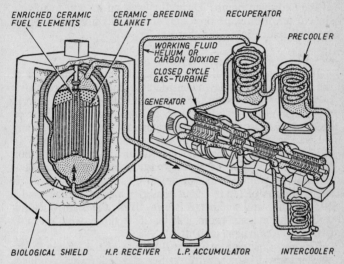

FIG. 5 The high-temperature ceramic-fuelled reactor—a type that may play an important part in future power-station design.

NEPTUNE and LIDO have related tasks to fulfil. The LIDO reactor derives its name from its peculiar design: it consists of a swimming-pool! Above the basin runs a trolley which supports the reactor core of enriched uranium, no larger than a tea chest. It has plate-type fuel elements instead of rods. While NEPTUNE is mainly used to develop a small, compact, efficient reactor for submarine and surface ship propulsion for the Admiralty, LIDO investigates the problems of shielding which are of major importance in a ship with nuclear propulsion. Shielding experiments are made by moving the trolley with the core in the water close to aluminium windows set in the wall of the basin.

Altogether, Harwell is working on seven main types of nuclear power stations—from improving the Calder Hall type which uses gas-cooled, graphite-moderated piles, to developing the fast breeder reactor which, in the period from 1970 onward, will increase our utilization of the basic nuclear fuel, uranium, a hundredfold. But beyond that stage there beckons the 'ultimate' energy source—thermonuclear fusion, the power of the hydrogen bomb. Harwell is well on its way to solving the cluster of intricate problems around this subject, to which we shall return in a later chapter.

Research into Atomic Structure

It is a curious fact that basic research into the structure of the atom has slowed down considerably since nuclear scientists became involved first in the production of bombs and then in the design of reactors. Especially Britain concentrated more on the practical aspects of nuclear energy while America and Russia spent at least some money on new research tools. In 1957, however, the British Government allotted £7 million for the construction of a new 'particle accelerator', a 7000-million-volt proton synchrotron, to be set up at Harwell. It should be completed by 1960, housed in a circular room under 10 ft of earth and a ceiling 4 ft 6 in. thick; the main shielding wall of the magnet room will be 28 ft thick, with movable blocks up to a height of 10 ft.

The new machine, which will be one of the largest in the Western world—the bevatron at Berkeley, California, produces an energy of 6000 electron-volt—is designed to create a beam of atomic particles: very fast protons, or nuclei of hydrogen atoms, which will be shot at other nuclear particles to study their interaction. For there are still many uncertainties about the structure of the nucleus, which the machine may help to clarify.

Since Professor E. O. Lawrence set up his first small cyclotron in the early 1930s, the power and design of these machines have undergone a great many changes, but not their basic principle, that of artificial acceleration of particles to very high speeds—they are the real 'atom smashers', magnetic racetracks where protons are made to collide with other matter. But to-day they can be used to produce artificially the sub-atomic particles, still somewhat mysterious, which have been discovered in cosmic rays. These particles, called mesons, are like sparks struck in the collision, whirlpools of magnetic force, with a lifetime of only a hundredth of a millionth of a second; then they change into another particle, and after that into yet another.

Where will it all lead? We do not know. Once again atomic Science is on the threshold of virgin land. Dr Robert J. Oppenheimer, director of the Los Alamos establishment during the creation of the atom bomb, said already in 1953: 'One may always hold that the true atoms, the immutable, hard atoms, have so far eluded physical discovery, but they are nevertheless there, and only when they are found will physics be dealing with the ultimate reality. Beyond that, one can hold that, although they have not been found by physical experiment and may never be found, they are the underlying reality in terms of which all else, including the world of physics, is to be understood.'

This sounds a little mysterious, almost mystical; but Professor R. E. Peierls of Birmingham University, also one of the fathers of the atom bomb, elaborated the subject in these terms: 'This new field of study goes beyond the structure of the nucleus and relates to the origin of the pieces of which a nucleus is made. . . . It is hoped that the results of work with the new machines may also help to solve the problem of the forces which hold the nucleus together. . . . The purpose served by such machines now appears quite academic. While we can foresee no practical application, the lesson of atomic energy should be that there is no telling where new knowledge may take us.'

Professor Peierls was referring to already existing accelerating machines such as the one in the physics department of his own university, which can bring protons to a speed of nine-tenths the speed of light. Russia has more powerful accelerators than anything existing in the West, and it may well be that the next great discovery in the field of the atomic nucleus may come from there. The most powerful machine, however, will be the one under construction at Geneva for Euratom, the community of European nuclear research nations; it will accelerate protons to 25,000 million electron-volts.

The Harwell synchrotron will be a most valuable tool of research for the study of the meson. Is it, as some scientists believe, the 'glue' that holds the nucleus together? 'Heavy' mesons, a thousand times heavier than electrons, were found in the cosmic rays that continually fall on the earth, coming from some distant interstellar space. They are more intense at high altitudes—Professor Auguste Piccard made his stratosphere balloon ascents and the sputniks were sent into their orbits to discover more about these rays, and permanent laboratories to catch them on photographic plates have been established on the Jungfraujoch in the Alps, at the Pic du Midi in the Pyrenees, and on the roof of London University's Senate House, to mention only a few places. Mesons as main constituents of these rays, which undergo great changes when they enter the earth's atmosphere, were identified and named as far back as 1947, and a few years later the scientists working with the bevatron at Berkeley succeeded in producing heavy mesons artificially in a continuous stream by making fast protons hit a piece of copper.

In 1955 this team surprised the scientific world with another great achievement. They discovered a nuclear particle whose existence had been suspected for a quarter of a century: the 'anti-proton'. It is in many ways similar to the proton, but instead of carrying a positive electric charge it has a negative one of exactly the same strength. But the anti-proton, in contrast to the proton, is very unstable; when an antiproton collides with a proton it annihilates itself—and the result of the collision is the birth of one pair of mesons!

The existence of positrons, or electrons with a positive electrical charge, has been known since 1932; and there is evidence that the neutron, too, may have its 'opposite number', a neutron with reversed magnetic polarity.

What does it all mean? Some physicists believe that somewhere in the universe there are worlds consisting of 'antimatter'—anti-protons, positive electrons, reversed-polarity neutrons. When matter meets anti-matter, so these physicists say, they annihilate one another in a release of energy comparable to that of an H-bomb. This must have happened in 1908 when a huge meteor crashed in Siberia; it left some big craters, enormous devastation was caused in a radius of 40 miles—but not the tiniest piece of the meteor has ever been found.

There are many more problems to solve until Science finds the key to what Professor Oppenheimer has called 'the true

atom'. There is, for instance, the recently discovered phenomenon that Nature is 'lopsided', that the atoms are spinning in
one direction, and that radio-active atoms throw out their
electrons backward in that direction. Two young Chinese-born
American physicists, Dr Lee and Dr Yang, received the 1957
Nobel Prize for their work on this 'puzzling lack of symmetry'
in Nature's atomic processes, and nuclear research workers are
now greatly excited about these unexpected discoveries.
Everywhere, 'spinning' experiments with mesons, cobalt isotopes and other atomic particles are going on at full speed.

Practical research helps the scientists to arrive at an under-
standing of the newly discovered atomic particles, and of the
unpredictable way in which the nuclear world seems to behave. The theory announced by Professor W. Heisenberg, of
Heidelberg, and Professor W. Pauli, of Zürich, in 1958 must
be regarded as a most important step in this direction. It
attempts to derive the properties of all the atomic particles
from an equation or physical law of a single unified form.
Heisenberg–Pauli's theory will influence nuclear research for
a long time, but one immediate consequence was that the fact
of the nuclear 'spin' has been put on a firm theoretical foundation instead of haunting the laboratories as a freakish whim of
Nature.

Such efforts are now facilitated in Britain by a new body, set
up in 1957—the Rutherford Institute for Nuclear Research.
It provides universities and other institutions with assistance
and equipment which are beyond their scope. The new proton-
synchrotron at Harwell is being built for the RINR, which
should help to keep Britain in the forefront of nuclear progress.

IV

POWER AND PLENTY

FROM THE beginning of time men have tried to harness the forces of Nature. Civilization began when they first tamed the fire to warm their caves and cook their food. Wild animals were forced under the yoke to supplement human muscle-power. The wind was used to propel ships, the waters of the rushing stream made to turn the grind-stone. For thousands of years these additional sources of energy remained the only ones available to toiling mankind, but people who were strong or rich enough to acquire slaves made them do all the heavy manual work. The general level of production—to use a modern term—was, therefore, low, and so was the standard of living, except for the slave-owning minority.

The first radical change came when James Watt built his steam-engine at the end of the 18th century. There are two reasons why this invention was of greater importance than any before in the history of civilization: it unlocked a vast storehouse of energy—coal, wood, oil—by providing a practical means of turning heat into mechanical power; and it put such great forces at Man's disposal that the production and distribution of goods, travel and communication accelerated beyond his most daring dreams within two or three generations. Society in the western world underwent a thorough transformation; we call it the Industrial Revolution. It was certainly a mixed blessing, and we cannot claim that the machine age has made mankind more peaceful and contented than the period of feudalism that preceded it. Perhaps we have not yet adapted ourselves to the notion that the age-old scramble for the manger is out of date, that there is enough to go round, enough for everybody if we distribute our new wealth in a fair and reasonable way, instead of frittering it away in preparation for another war.

Man's appetite for energy, ever since it was roused, has been insatiable. Within the last hundred years electricity, internal-combustion engines, and now atomic energy have added to his power supply. During that period the amount of commercially produced energy at his disposal increased by twenty-four times. It is not merely a coincidence that during the same period the population of the world increased more than ever before; it just about doubled. This means that the amount of energy available for each person in the world is now twelve times greater than in 1860.

But here we must not generalize, for large areas of the world —including the most densely populated, like India and China —have seen hardly any mechanization of their daily chores. The plough is still drawn by men and oxen, water still carried on the heads of women all over Africa and Asia; the average American citizen has about twenty times as much energy at his disposal as his contemporary in Kashmir or Bechuanaland. Once, the standard of living reached by a country used to be reckoned by the number of pieces of soap per head of population; now we have a more reliable unit of measurement: the energy available per head, which indicates the level of production. And that means food, clothing, housing—everything that goes into the daily lives of the people, and everything that may be exported to other countries in exchange for additional goods and services. The horsepower a man controls and uses is directly related to his standard of living.

The Industrial Revolution was made by a relatively small group of people—the manufacturers and their bankers, inspired by no greater ideal than that of improving their own standard of living by making more money. The Second Industrial Revolution, which we are now experiencing, is of a much more intricate nature. Our own western standards are so high that there is not a great deal of scope for industrial expansion; on the contrary, more energy, more automation may result in serious economic crises and social upheavals. But there are these vast, under-developed areas of the world which are crying out for energy, goods, and services; raising their standard of living is the great job the world will have to do in the last four decades of our century, not just for idealistic or humanitarian reasons, but because this is the only way in which industrialized countries can find an outlet for their surplus production, and because modern transport and communication have made our world one world. If we let one part of it go hungry much longer, we ourselves will eventually starve.

Before the advent of atomic energy the under-developed countries had no other chance of creating more energy than by the same slow process by which it was done in Europe and America during the last hundred years. Harnessing great rivers for hydro-electric power is a lengthy and costly job; besides, many countries have no great rivers to harness. Dr H. J. Bhabha, the leading Indian scientist and President of the International Conference on Atomic Energy in Geneva in 1955, said that India had only enough potential resources of energy to sustain an economy equivalent to that of the USA for ten years. Thus, even if India succeeded in increasing her energy production by so radical a degree, she could not maintain this expansion with conventional sources of energy.

It is here that atomic energy will make all the difference. Power from nuclear fission can be created without the harnessing of rivers or the ceaseless digging of coal. All that is required is a few tons of uranium or thorium—and the technical know-how. Within three years a major nuclear power station can be built anywhere in the world. It is, therefore, in our own interest to export to these countries the know-how if they require it, the necessary raw material and equipment if they cannot produce them on the spot—and then give them credit and sympathetic help. Within a surprisingly short time they will be our customers, suppliers, and friends.

These lines of thought are, in fact, being followed up by the three great atomic powers: America, Russia, and Britain. There is already some rivalry among them as to who will be the under-developed countries' best friend. The United Nations can, and does, provide a platform for collective action; but the atomic powers are still somewhat suspicious of this new medium for international cooperation, and hesitate to give it the full support it needs. However, a great deal is already being done in this field; we shall return to the subject later. First of all let us examine the position of a major industrial nation which might have been reduced to insignificance through lack of energy if nuclear power had not provided an answer to her problem.

Great Britain built its industry exclusively on coal; only during the last few decades has oil played an appreciable rôle in supplying part of its power requirements. Unlike the USA, the United Kingdom has no oilfields within its own borders; it has to import oil from the Middle East and America. Its coal resources, on the other hand, may be exhausted within our own lifetime; at any rate, the coal that can be mined economically will last only until about 1980 if the present speed of increase in energy consumption—2·5–3 per cent per annum—is maintained. If coal and oil were the only fuels available to Britain, which has hardly any hydro-electric power, she might soon be unable to meet her increasing energy needs, and drop out of the ranks of the highly industrialized nations with a comfortable standard of living.

For this reason, Britain has been the first nation to adopt a plan for supplanting coal by atomic energy, and to begin with its execution. This plan aims at completing by the end of 1965 sufficient nuclear-power stations to deliver a total output of 5–6 million kw, equivalent to 18 million tons of coal. Just in time, one might add; for it has been estimated that there would be a shortage of 17 million tons of coal for power-station supply by 1965. By 1975, 40 per cent of Britain's electric current should be coming from nuclear energy. It lies within the nature of atomic-power production that it will also become cheaper as time and development go on. Furthermore, it will help in the production of other fuels by providing direct heat to carbonize coal in the gas works, and energy to crack oil in the refineries.

But Britain will also need less oil. In 1957 the Government warned the oil companies to cut their long-term plans for import. According to earlier plans, oil imports were to have risen from 28 million tons in 1957–58 to 50 million tons in 1965. Now the need will be for only 41 million tons. Looking still farther ahead, Britain's entire energy requirements by 1975 may be the equivalent of 360 million tons of coal; nearly half of these requirements will be met by nuclear power. Theoretically, all of it could be provided by burning a mere 250 tons of uranium and/or thorium a year, provided that the breeding technique is by then fully developed.

At present, plans for building at least twelve nuclear-power stations by 1965, providing a quarter of Britain's electricity needs, are being worked out. Every nine months or so the Central Electricity Authority lets a new contract for the construction of an atomic-power station.

"Fourteen years after Fermi built his crude atomic pile on the football ground of the University of Chicago we completed the first nuclear-power station in Britain using two atomic piles of the same general type as that of Fermi to produce heat and so to generate steam and 70,000 kw of electricity. By 1961 we shall have seven nuclear-power stations operating in Britain, generating over 1 million kw, and by 1965 we are likely to be producing a quarter of our electricity from nuclear-power stations. This is a remarkable example of scientific discovery followed by technological development—forty years of pure research with no particular objective in mind, only the interest of seeking out the innermost secrets of Nature. And then suddenly the curtain is lifted and practical applications appear—almost overnight," said Sir John Cockcroft in October, 1957, talking to the boys of Hampton Grammar School. "And not only shall we achieve an important addition to our energy supplies but the world as a whole has increased its reserves of energy at least 30-fold; so instead of coal and oil supplies beginning to run out in one or two centuries, uranium and thorium can carry us on for a thousand years or so, and long before that I expect we will have harnessed the nuclear energy of light elements by the fusion process and solved the energy problem for as long as Man exists."

We have come a long way from the first Industrial Revolution when private enterprise was the only spur to greater productivity. We are thinking in terms of national and world requirements, and we are thinking of the distant future. We are even prepared to invest money in it.

The economics of nuclear power are somewhat different from those of other forms of energy. If you start digging for coal, your initial investment is relatively small, and your returns start almost immediately; but as the shafts and seams lengthen and the coalface recedes farther and farther from the pithead your costs mount considerably, and your coal gets dearer. From 1945 to 1965 Britain's investment in her coal mines will amount to about £2000 million.

It is just the opposite with nuclear power. Your initial investment is considerable, and you have to build a formidable reactor station and charge it with expensive fuel before you start getting your money back by selling electric current. But as time goes on you will produce not only electricity but also new nuclear fuel. Your income will therefore rise and your costs go down.

This is reflected in the financial side of Britain's atomic-power programme. The total investment for the period ending in 1965 will be £3350 million, which is £750 million more than it would have been if coal-burning power stations were built. The power stations will receive a first charge of uranium fuel at a cost of £177 million (included in the above-mentioned figure).

Once the power stations get going, however, the cost of energy generated by them will fall steeply. The United Kingdom Atomic Energy Authority aims at generating electricity at a cost of 0·4d. per kilowatt/hour, which is less than two-thirds of the cost of coal-produced current, by 1965; another quarter of a century later the cost of nuclear power would be no more than three-eighths of power from coal-fired stations. Already during the period 1960–65 the output of individual nuclear-power stations is likely to increase to such an extent that capital costs will fall; nuclear-power costs should reach parity with coal-power costs by 1962.

The reason for this calculation is that with a nuclear-power station about 65 per cent of the total costs is for capital charges, which amount to no more than 25 per cent in the case of a coal-burning station—the cost of installation per kilowatt is about £150 with the former against £50 with the latter. But the £150 includes the first fuel charge, which will last for a very long time —at least for six or seven years—while the old-type power station needs incessant shovelling of coal (or feeding of oil). Therefore the cost of nuclear power is mainly made up of interest for the capital outlay, maintenance, and depreciation, while the largest item in the cost of coal-generated power is fuel.

There is one point about the switch-over to atomic power which may become important in the distant future. Some of the old-type power stations will no doubt become redundant. Can they be converted into nuclear-power stations? This is a technical problem which has to be solved. The temperature and pressure of steam in the two types of power plant are very different, but developments may make it possible to convert one into the other at much lower cost than the building of new atomic stations would require.

In the story of Man's utilization of energy, the name of Calder Hall plays a part similar to James Watt's steam engine. The world's first full-size nuclear-power station, though it will be superseded by installations of a greatly advanced design, will never be ousted from the annals of human achievement, and the date of its official opening, October 17, 1956, will rank among the most important dates in technical history.

Oddly enough, Calder Hall was not meant to become a power station, at least not in the first place. In February, 1953, the British Government asked the Atomic Energy Authority to speed up its production of plutonium for nuclear weapons. In response, Harwell recommended a plan which had already been studied for some time—that of combining a plutonium-producing plant with a power station. The site which was eventually chosen for this station fitted in with the original purpose of plutonium production: Calder Hall in Cumberland, opposite the Windscale works, which had been making plutonium for some time.

Calder Hall—or 'Calder A' and 'Calder B', as the twin stations are called officially—is the simplest type of atomic-power station—some call it the crudest. In an old-type power station, steam to operate the turbo-generators is raised by burning coal or oil under boilers. In Calder Hall steam is produced by using the energy of a nuclear chain reaction to heat carbon-dioxide gas; this is sent to the heat exchanger, a device which fulfils the job of a conventional boiler by turning water into steam. The turbines and dynamos are the same as in any coal-burning power station.

The essential novelty, then, is the reactor. There are four of them at Calder—'A' and 'B'. Each is contained in a giant steel cylinder 37 ft in diameter. Inside is a pile of pure graphite, the material of which pencil leads are made. 1760 vertical channels have been bored through it; the 'fuel'—bars of uranium metal in magnesium alloy sheaths—is stacked in some of the channels, while the control rods, which are made of boron steel, are hanging in the other ones. The sheathing of the fuel rods is necessary to prevent the atoms of the dangerously radio-active fission products—the 'ashes' of the fission process—from getting into the coolant flow and being carried out of the reactor. There is, however, the risk that the magnesium 'cans', which absorb neutrons, may develop a leak, and it is essential to discover at the earliest possible moment if this has happened. For that reason a small sample of the coolant gas is fed into a Geiger monitor, and if any radio-activity above a certain level is detected, the reactor must be stopped.

As soon as the control rods are pulled out, the chain reaction begins. Uranium nuclei split up into radio-active waste products and penetrating radiations are given out. The uranium bars get hot and are allowed to reach a temperature of 400° C. The heat from the uranium, of which each reactor contains 120 tons, is removed by the coolant, carbon-dioxide gas compressed to a pressure of 100 lb per square inch, about seven times that of the atmosphere. The gas is pumped through the graphite core by four circulating blowers. It enters the bottom of the core at 140° C and leaves at the top at 336° C.

The hot gas is fed by four outlet pipes, each about $4\frac{1}{2}$ ft in diameter, into four large cylinders set at the corners of the reactor. These heat exchangers are, in principle, simple devices. Each is criss-crossed by several miles of stainless-steel piping through which water is circulating. The hot carbon dioxide is blown round these pipes, which have many metal stubs welded to them. Inside the pipes the water turns to steam, which is directed into the turbines. The eight Calder Hall steam turbines can generate 184,000 kw of electricity.

But Calder Hall is also a plutonium-making plant, though not nearly as efficient as Dounreay or even the 'old' Windscale factory. Plutonium, as we know, is made from the U-238 atoms mixed with the fissile U-235 ones in the fuel elements when they undergo a chain reaction. Calder Hall, however, is not a 'fast breeder', like Dounreay; most of its neutrons, moderated by the graphite, are slow. It is estimated that for every 100 atoms of U-235 burnt in the reactors, 80-85 plutonium atoms will be formed, compared with about twice as many at Dounreay. If the fuel-rods were left undisturbed they would give off heat for a number of years until the uranium and plutonium is 'burnt out'. But the military want their plutonium, so the fuel-rods are taken out after a few months and Windscale will do the rest by extracting the plutonium from them. The original ton of natural uranium yields at least $12\frac{1}{2}$ lb of plutonium.

Here we have, in a nutshell, the conflict between the

destructive and the productive sides of nuclear-energy utilization. Although it is true to say that there might be no atomic energy today if the war had not caused the Allied governments to sponsor the atom bomb, peaceful developments since 1945 have been very much slower than they might have been if the making of nuclear bombs had been stopped then. Calder Hall is an excellent example of the conflict between the two parties. Every 140 lb of uranium contains 1 lb of U-235, which could be burnt up to do the work of 3 million lb of coal. Then there is the plutonium, which could be burnt to produce more heat and more plutonium. Each ton of uranium would be able to do the work of 50,000 tons of coal before all its uranium and plutonium were burnt up. But at Calder Hall nuclear reaction is stopped long before all the U-235 is used up, and the plutonium extracted—most of it to be used for nuclear weapons.

Of course, if there were an international agreement to dismantle all nuclear weapons (and if this agreement were carried out), the world would find itself in the possession of an enormous store of high-grade atomic fuel. Prices would then probably drop like those for army surplus socks or tables, and we would all benefit.

The Problem of Safety

Considering that Calder Hall was a large-scale venture without precedent, one might have expected all kinds of unpleasant surprises. But everything went more or less smoothly. Out of 10,000 fuel elements only three failed during the first eight months of operation, which began in October, 1956. The first reactor to go into commission was never out of action for more than 10 per cent of its time (15 per cent had been expected). One snag was that some carbon-dioxide gas from the cooling system escaped into the atmosphere for a while, but the leak was eventually found and stopped. Another mishap in the beginning of the power-station's life occurred when fuel elements of canned uranium rods were stacked on top of each other in columns of six. The influence of weight and radiation caused the lower units in the stack to bend a little. The remedy—the fitting of support struts—was easy to find.

"We have found only one unexpected phenomenon in the reactor behaviour," said Sir John Cockcroft. "Experiments at Harwell during the last years predicted that uranium rods under stress would be more plastic and would bow more rapidly due to their irradiation in the reactor. We shut down the Calder Hall reactor in November, 1956, and examined a number of fuel elements and found that this bowing was actually occurring."

Thereby hangs an interesting tale. As soon as the reactor had been shut down according to plan for this investigation, newspapers on the European Continent published sensational stories about the complete failure of Britain's first atomic-power station only a month after the Queen had officially opened it. These stories were traced back to American sources, and they had a purpose: that of making potential buyers of atomic equipment in Europe suspicious towards British achievements in this field. Needless to say that American competitors were behind the manœuvre, backed by German coal-mine owners who were against the whole scheme of introducing atomic power in their country.

Perhaps the greatest anxiety in connection with nuclear-energy installations concerns the safety of the people working in the plant and of the public in general. At Calder Hall the major problem was the protection of workers against the risk of exposure to radiation from the reactor. We know that the extent to which radiation of the body can be tolerated is limited; the result of exceeding the limit may be an incurable disease of the blood, leukæmia, a cancerous increase in the number of white corpuscles and bone cancer.

Two main types of radiation from the reactor, the neutrons and the gamma rays which are given off during the fission process (the latter are a special danger when fissile material is removed from the core), must be kept in mind from the very beginning of power-station design. The first principle is that of 'biological shielding': radiation-absorbing barriers must be placed between the source of radiation and the worker. Concrete, lead, or steel are suitable materials; the thickness of the shield depends on the intensity of radiation. The Calder Hall reactors are enclosed in walls of concrete 7 ft thick. Irradiated fuel elements are removed from the reactors in thick lead boxes.

Another safety measure is the limiting of the duration of certain jobs which entail exposure to abnormally intense radiation. This factor, too, must be considered already at the design stage, and as many operations as possible must be carried out either automatically or by remote control.

What about the risk of a thermal reactor getting out of control? The Windscale accident in the autumn of 1957, which we described in detail in the foregoing chapter, made many people wonder whether this atomic age might not be rather hazardous for the ordinary citizen even without a nuclear war, and apart from H-bomb-test risks. But there is certainly no possibility of a reactor exploding, and very little of its getting out of control—'excursion' is the American euphemism for such happenings. However, there is an automatic shut-down arrangement which drops the control rods rapidly into the pile if certain instruments at critical points in the reactor record some potentially dangerous development. And there is, of course, a control-room where the operators on duty are watching the dials, and there are alarm bells which ring when something tends to go wrong. All the operators have to do is press a few buttons to cope with the emergency.

Dangerous Waste

All the same, we may not so easily get used to having these uncanny giants of power stations in our midst, and the planning authorities are prepared to take notice of our anxieties and susceptibilities when deciding on power-station sites. There is some difference of opinion about this; not everybody is happy to know that the reactors are safely out of the way at isolated places. The authorities have been called 'vandals' bent on destroying the wild beauty and quiet of these remote parts of the British Isles. But we can't have it both ways, and it may be less unfair to annoy a few nature lovers than to make the population of a whole town or suburb nervous. After all, the voices which objected to the beauty-destroying railways in the last century died away within a surprisingly short time; and a well-designed atomic-power station may even add to the charm of a landscape—perhaps more so than an ugly 19th-century railway station.

For many years to come, therefore, the siting of atomic establishments with reactors may be governed by the notion that, despite all safeguards, there might occur an escape of radio-activity. The reactor should be in a place where any restrictions that might ever become necessary in the interests of public safety would cause as little inconvenience as possible to the population. The tendency has been to site nuclear-power stations near the coast where there are unlimited supplies of water, but it has been said that there is no technical reason why a Calder Hall type of station should not be built next door to the Houses of Parliament in Westminster.

There are, of course, safe and unsafe types of reactors. Water-cooled piles—such as those built for plutonium production at Hanford, USA—are inherently unsafe because the water used as a coolant is a more powerful absorber of neutrons than the carbon-dioxide gas at Calder Hall. If any of the cooling water was lost in the reactor the neutrons which would have been absorbed by it would remain inside and increase the activity of the reactor.

Water, therefore, is a potential source of danger in all atomic establishments. At Harwell all the water from the reactors and laboratories is treated over and over again and pumped from one tank to the other until most radio-active elements have been removed; only then is it discharged into the river. In all establishments processing radio-active matter or experimenting with it there is always a large volume of liquid waste which must not be discharged directly into any water system where it might be used for drinking-water. The aim, therefore, is to concentrate the radio-active matter from these effluents into as small a volume as possible, and either store it in special tanks or discharge it in diluted form into the sea at a point where there is no hazard to fishing or bathing.

Gaseous waste and fine dust from reactors which use air as a coolant and from chemical processing plants are not a particularly great hazard. Most of the isotopes discharged in this form are short-lived, and once they are released by way of a chimney-stack they decay fairly quickly in the atmosphere. Filters in the stacks reduce the discharged radio-active solids to a minimum.

There are all kinds of solid objects which may have become contaminated in the course of work with radio-active matter, from gloves to glasses and from tools to plants used in biological experiments. Most of them can be incinerated to reduce the bulk of radio-active matter, and the ash can then be stored away safely.

The trouble ensuing when, in spite of all precautions, one of the workers of a radio-active installation becomes contaminated was demonstrated a few years ago, when a night watchman at Hanford was found to have radio-active hands. He was cross-examined: where could he have 'caught' it? Eventually he remembered that he had found a broken spanner in a bin and taken it home.

The decontamination squad was mobilised, and raced to the man's home, eight miles from Hanford. The Geiger counters ticked away as soon as the specialists approached the front door; the whole house was already infected. The man's family was at once evacuated and isolated. The squad, clad in protective clothing from tip to toe, started a thorough 'spring cleaning'. Everything, including the hapless night watchman himself, was scrubbed down with soap and water. The central heating system, which had absorbed the bulk of the alpha particles carried into the place with the spanner, was torn out and destroyed. Pots and pans, household linen, clothes, cutlery, curtains, cushions went the same way. The night watchman was kept in solitary confinement for a week, surrounded by Geiger counters. He was not permitted to shave because of the danger that some alpha particles might get into his bloodstream if he cut himself. He was eventually allowed to return to work when his radio-activity had gone down to normal, and there were no after-effects; but the case received much publicity by the Hanford safety officers as an example of the danger of picking up anything in a nuclear establishment.

Sometimes the picking-up may be done quite involuntarily, as in the case of little Joke Haanschoten, a four-year-old girl in the small Dutch town of Putten. She had been treated for some slight nasal trouble in the University hospital at Utrecht, but on returning home she became violently sick. The mother, believing this to be the harmless aftermath of the operation, burned the stuff which the girl had ejected in the stove, and later the cinders were thrown on the rubbish-heap in the garden.

Meanwhile, Joke's condition had grown worse, and the doctor was called. He discovered that the minute head of a radium needle had broken off in the girl's nose. She had ejected it when being sick, but by now the damage had been done—she, the six other members of her family, the whole house, and a large part of Putten, where the radio-active ashes from the garden had blown, were contaminated.

Within an hour the health authorities had sealed off the

84

house and garden, posted white-coated officials with Geiger counters all over the district, and taken the whole family and fifteen other people to the isolation ward of the nearest hospital. Signposts with barbed wire, guarded by policemen, warned everybody approaching the street with the Haanschotens' house, DANGER TO LIFE—KEEP OFF. The butcher, the baker, the milkman and many other people who had been in touch with the family were ordered to bury their coins in the woods. Cats had to be destroyed, clogs burned.

The upheaval at Putten lasted for many days, and even then no one could say for sure if the 'cleaning' of people and things had prevented serious harm. It all seemed like a local dress rehearsal of some future nuclear war. Yet there was no more than 50 mg of radium in the needle head—infinitely less radioactive matter than the 'fall-out' of a bomb.

Several British establishments near the coast have pipelines for discharging liquid effluents into the sea, but this is looked upon as a makeshift arrangement. It has been calculated that if the development of atomic energy goes on at the same rate as during the last few years the radio-active 'background' of the sea would be raised seriously through such discharges. A more satisfactory way is that of burying the waste material in cement cases and dropping them far out in the sea at a depth of 10,000 ft.

Radio-active caesium and strontium are usually separated from the rest of the fission products; caesium is used increasingly in medicine while strontium is mostly concentrated and stored until activity has decayed to a low enough level for discharge into the sea. As many isotopes can be extremely useful (see next chapter), the key to the whole waste problem may lie in their beneficial application. Another idea is that of storing waste in disused mines; but there will have to be a most careful selection of such pits. The Safety Executive Committee of the United Kingdom Atomic Energy Authority, which was formed in 1957, is the department responsible for all these measures.

It is a psychologically interesting point that the constant watchfulness required by all personnel in nuclear establishments has made them more accident-conscious than workers in many other industries. This alertness in the presence of such risks as radiation and 'criticality'—the danger of some radioactive matter starting a chain reaction of its own—also extends to general hazards, from that of slipping on freshly waxed lino to getting an electric shock from a badly insulated flex, with the result that the atomic industry has a better accident record than any other comparable industry today.

Towards Abundance of Energy

Britain is the first country in the world to launch a national programme for generating electricity from nuclear power. Calder Hall has been given a companion station, Chapelcross, also with four reactors for combined plutonium production and electricity generation; the last of them will become critical in 1959.

BRITAIN'S NUCLEAR POWER STATION PROGRAMME:

The Next Stage

After the completion of Calder B and Chapelcross, these stations will be built:

Berkeley, Gloucestershire. Output: 275,000 kw. In operation in 1961.
Bradwell, Essex. Output: 300,000 kw. In operation in 1961.
Hunterston, Ayrshire. Output: 320,000 kw.
Hinkley Point, Somerset. Output: 500,000 kw.[1]
Trawsfynnyd, Caernarvon. Output: 500,000 kw.
Northern Ireland. Output: 150,000 kw.
Dungeness, Kent. Output: 500,000 kw.

After 1975, only nuclear-power stations will be constructed in Great Britain.

[1] This station will be the largest in the world at the time of its completion. It may set the standard for the size of nuclear-power stations for many years.

The next set of stations to be built will have two reactors each for electricity generation only. They will each use 250 tons of uranium metal per reactor (Calder Hall has 120 tons per reactor). By increasing the pressure of the carbon-dioxide gas, the coolant, by 50 per cent, twice as much heat

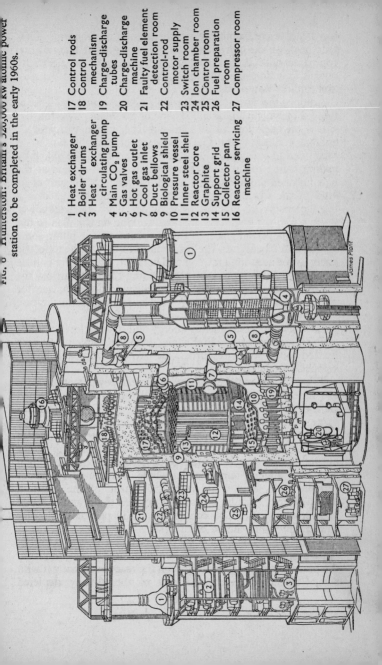

FIG. 8   Humerston: Britain's 320,000 kw atomic power station to be completed in the early 1960s.

1 Heat exchanger
2 Boiler drums
3 Heat exchanger circulating pump
4 Main CO₂ pump
5 Gas valves
6 Hot gas outlet
7 Cool gas inlet
8 Duct bellows
9 Biological shield
10 Pressure vessel
11 Inner steel shell
12 Reactor core
13 Graphite
14 Support grid
15 Collector pan
16 Reactor servicing machine
17 Control rods
18 Control mechanism
19 Charge-discharge tubes
20 Charge-discharge machine
21 Faulty fuel element detection room
22 Control-rod motor supply
23 Switch room
24 Ion chamber room
25 Control room
26 Fuel preparation room
27 Compressor room

James Plant

can be extracted from the reactor per ton of uranium. This, together with the more than 100 per cent greater mass of fuel compared with that at Calder Hall, results in an electricity output four times greater, reactor for reactor, than at Britain's first nuclear-power station.

Among the 'second-generation' power stations, Trawsfynnyd in North Wales will be one of the most powerful. Its site is on the shore of an artificial lake, which can provide enough cooling water for a capacity of 500,000 kw. It is scheduled to start operation in 1962, when it will be linked by overhead line to the 275,000-volt transmission system at the new pumped-storage station near Ffestiniog, the biggest of its kind in the world. The lake was created in the 1920s as a storage reservoir for the Maentwrog hydro-electric power station, and the engineers are now working on the plan to use the off-peak period power of the nuclear station to pump some of the water back into the reservoir; in other words, electric energy produced by Trawsfynnyd at night, when there is little demand, will be 'stored' by replenishing the reservoir for the hydro-electric station, thus providing additional power for Maentwrog. This system may also be practicable in the case of one or two Scottish nuclear-power stations.

In some countries nuclear energy and hydro-electric power may appear as rivals; in Britain, however, which has very limited water-power resources, the two may very well be developed together on suitable sites.

The question may be asked why nuclear-power stations with ten times the output of Calder Hall cannot be constructed right away. The answer is: we must first wait for the development of reactors, especially fuel elements, which can be operated at a much higher temperature—up to 500 or even 600° C. This would make it possible to increase the power output of a two-reactor station to 800,000 or perhaps 1 million kw. The higher temperature would require the use of ceramic fuels, oxides and carbides, instead of the uranium metal. It may then be necessary to enrich the uranium metal by increasing its U-235 content by 10–30 per cent; alternatively, plutonium can be used.

When the second stage of power-station development in Britain is under way there should be enough plutonium from the first stage to 'recycle' it through the reactors, mixing it with some 'virgin' uranium and part of the already depleted uranium. "This would mean", said Sir John Cockcroft, "that our feed of natural uranium could be reduced by a factor of about three so that this might be a great economy in uranium utilization. We are now working on the technology of recycling plutonium. Plutonium is a toxic material, so it would have to be mixed with uranium inside closed boxes, using remote control operation. By 1965, when we are likely to be recycling plutonium, we might well be using ceramic fuels such as plutonium oxide and uranium oxide, which would simplify fabrication."

On the other hand, the Industrial Group of the United Kingdom Atomic Energy Authority at Risley is considering a smaller and cheaper power station of the sodium-graphite type, working with slightly enriched uranium; the first research reactor of this type may become critical in 1959, and a full-scale power station of this type may be designed if the tests prove satisfactory. We have already explained that sodium, in the form of a metallic liquid, is a better heat-transfer medium than carbon-dioxide gas, so that heat can be produced at a higher rate per ton of uranium. This will make it possible to reduce the size of the reactor considerably, and build a small, compact, and inexpensive power station with 100,000 kw capacity.

Atomic Energy in America

Nearly three dozen countries are at present operating, building, or planning reactors, or at least conducting nuclear research. But only three countries—Britain, the USA, and the Soviet Union—can be regarded as leading in this new field of industry; it is no mere coincidence that they are also the only countries which have developed and stored nuclear weapons—at least at the time of writing. However, any day some other government may surprise us with the claim to have produced atomic or thermo-nuclear bombs and missiles, which in the diplomatic language of our age is identical with the claim to be in the running for world leadership. France appears to be the next candidate, with Western Germany, Canada, and Sweden following at some distance.

In the USA the development of nuclear energy for peaceful purposes was comparatively slow until the introduction of the Atomic Energy Law of 1954, which lifted some of the security bars that had prevented private industry from using the 'know-how' of the strictly guarded military establishments. The

Atomic Energy Commission is also allowed to export nuclear fuels and reactor components to 'friendly' nations. In fact, many agreements exist for co-operation in this field between the USA and countries throughout the world; however, the exchange of information, especially with Britain, has never been

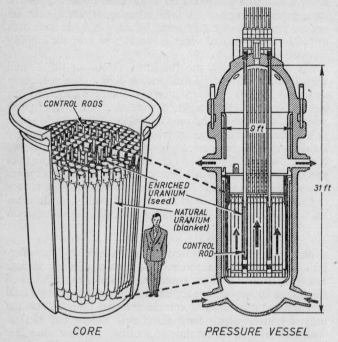

FIG. 7   The pressurized-water reactor of America's first commercial nuclear power station at Shippingport, on the Ohio river.

really satisfactory, despite quite a number of agreements. The American authorities are rather sensitive to public opinion, which reacted to the discovery of some cases of atomic and political espionage with the demand that all 'classified' information should be withheld from Britain.

America has no immediate need for nuclear power, being in possession of much easily mineable coal and vast oil reserves within her own borders. But her energy requirements are rising very fast; besides, if you want to sell nuclear equipment abroad you must first show that you believe in it by installing it at home. America's first commercial power station has been built at Shippingport, on the Ohio River. It is less powerful than Calder Hall and develops only 60,000 kw of electricity, rising eventually to 100,000 kw. The reactor moderator and coolant is ordinary water at a pressure of 2000 lb per square inch and a temperature of 540° F (282° C). The pile, controlled by hafnium metal rods, uses two kinds of fuel elements, enriched uranium clad in a zirconium alloy and pellets of natural uranium oxide, also in zirconium alloy tubes. The 180,000-kw 'Dresden' power station near Chicago, using ordinary boiling water both as moderator and coolant, will be completed in 1960; a 275,000-kw power station—nuclear and oil-fired combined—will be built north of New York.

Although the pressurized-water type of reactor is neither very efficient nor very safe, it was decided to use it for the first large-scale plant because it was the type with which a great deal of operational experience has been gathered: the first atomic submarine, the *Nautilus* (which we shall describe in a later chapter), was equipped with it. Shippingport is certainly not an economical power station; the current it produces is several times more expensive than that of a coal-fired plant. But, then, economy has never been an important factor in American nuclear development; for instance, the diffusion plants alone—where the radio-active isotope is extracted from natural uranium—consume as much electricity as the whole of France!

As in Britain, thermal reactor research in America has branched out along various lines. Apart from the pressurized-water and boiling-water types, these reactors are being developed: sodium-cooled and graphite-moderated; fast breeder; organic-moderated; homogeneous; liquid-metal fuelled; gas-cooled; natural-uranium fuelled and heavy-water moderated. For some reason or other, the Calder Hall type of reactor is neglected in America. In terms of expenditure and the number of research and production establishments, the USA has the largest atomic-energy programme in the world; it will have swallowed more than £4000 million when completed, excluding private industrial investment. The wonderfully equipped Argonne National Laboratory, for instance, will have a £9 million nuclear accelerator, the world's biggest. The joint Atomic Energy Commission and industrial plants and laboratories occupy an area of 3200 square miles, spread over twenty-two states, and employing 107,000 people, but only 6000 of them are employed by the AEC itself (as compared with the 25,000 employees of Britain's AEA); the rest are workers, engineers, and scientists from the large industrial concerns such as the Union Carbide and Carbon Corporation, the Consolidated Edison Company, the Westinghouse Electric

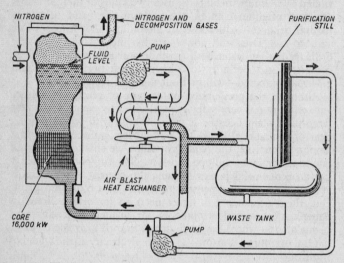

FIG. 8 The organic-moderated experimental reactor at the Testing Station of the U.S. Atomic Energy Commission in Idaho. It is used for developing economical atomic power plants.

Corporation, and many others. Altogether, seventy-five reactors were completed or in course of construction in industrial concerns in 1957–58.

America's atomic industry has developed from the gigantic wartime effort to produce the first atom bombs, and a major part of the research, development, and production programme is still a military one. As there is no pressing need for power stations, that part of the programme is being pursued at a more leisurely pace than in Britain. None of the six power stations now scheduled to be built in various states will produce more than 250,000 kw of electricity by nuclear energy, the average capacity being in the 100,000 kw region. Even when this programme has been completed—or rather, if, for at the time of writing most of it is still on paper—the contribution made to America's energy needs by nuclear power will be extremely small. But the USA will continue to lead the world in its output of fissile material. The vast Oak Ridge National Laboratory with its £120 million diffusion plant has now been supplemented by three further large diffusion plants at the Hanford and Savannah River sites; at Hanford alone eight big reactors are being used for plutonium production. As America's own requirements are now more than amply provided for, the rest of the world can buy fissile material from her on an increasing scale. Mr Jesse Johnson, Director of Raw Materials of the AEC, calculated that the Western world has now an output of 30,000 tons of uranium oxide per year, thanks to the release of atomic fuel by the USA.

Canada is in a similar position as the USA as far as her energy requirements are concerned: she has no need to be worried, especially as her hydro-electric power, actual and potential, is abundant. But she also has large deposits of uranium, and her close association with the early development of atomic energy during the war has prompted her to continue nuclear research. She has four experimental reactors in operation—one of them started up as early as September, 1945. Canada, which is at present experiencing the greatest industrial and economic expansion since the days of the Hudson's Bay Company, will very likely make extensive use of one of the most important features of nuclear power: that it can be applied where it is needed, independently of any mineral resources or geographic formations such as waterfalls. Atomic-power stations will probably be built where new industries require energy, such as the extraction of aluminium. That vast country may become a proving ground for the great attraction of atomic power—that it frees heavy industry from its dependence on those few parts of the world where coal and oil are abundant.

What are the Russians doing?

By 1965, when Britain will have 6 million kw, or 25 per cent of its total electricity consumption, from atomic power, the USA may not have much more than $1\frac{1}{2}$ million kw, or

93

$2\frac{1}{2}$ per cent. The Soviet Union, however, judging by various plans, speeches, and publications, will be as far advanced as Britain—in absolute if not relative figures. She, too, will produce some 5 or 6 million kw by 1965, but from no more than ten or a dozen power stations, which are scheduled to be larger than the British ones. They will provide 14–18 per cent of the energy needs of the Soviet Union. But, as in the case of Britain and America, atomic development for Russia is a political necessity as well as an economic one. Apart from her military programme, which seems to be very large indeed, she has a 'prestige' plan for exporting complete power stations and nuclear equipment to her allies and the 'uncommitted' nations, and she must demonstrate to them that she is technologically as advanced as her competitors. It is from this point of view that we must judge her power-development efforts.

The Russians like to claim that they were the first to build a nuclear-power station. This is true in so far as they completed their thermal pilot plant near Moscow in 1955, but with its output of a mere 5000 kw it cannot hold comparison with Calder Hall. Now they have opened a second one, also near Moscow, and two in the Ural Mountains are nearing completion; the combined output of these three will be in the region of $1\frac{1}{2}$ million kw.

These stations are Russia's 'first generation' and are of the graphite-moderated, ordinary-water-cooled type; the second generation will comprise at least one large boiling-heavy-water homogeneous reactor in which the nuclear fuel—U-233 derived from thorium—is suspended in the heavy water.

Russia is also building giant nuclear accelerators for basic research, including the utilization of thermo-nuclear—fusion —energy. Her research and development programme is closely linked with the work in her satellite countries; some of them, especially Czechoslovakia and Eastern Germany, supply her with abundant quantities of uranium. China, too, sends uranium to Russia, and in return the Russians are supplying these countries with experimental 2000-kw reactors. The great research centre at Dubna, on the Volga, is open to scientists and technicians from these countries; here they can see the 10,000-million-volt synchrotron, the largest of its kind in the world; there are plans to build one with 50,000 million volts energy.

Czechoslovakia, after Eastern Germany the most highly industrialized country in the Soviet orbit, is building a large nuclear-power station at Banska Bystrica, in Slovakia, to be completed in 1960; by 1965 the annual increase in electricity requirements will be wholly met by nuclear power.

France—the Runner-up

France may benefit from nuclear energy even before she operates the first atomic-power station of her own: the British and the French power grids may be linked so that the peak loads, which occur at different times in the two countries, can be more evenly distributed. Thus, Britain will get current from the hydro-electric stations in the Pyrenees, and France from Calder Hall.

The French are very conscious of the historical fact that radium and radio-activity was discovered on their soil. From Henri Becquerel to Frédéric Joliot-Curie, French scientists have always been in the forefront of nuclear research. Already under General de Gaulle's wartime Government a special State Department, the *Commissariet à l'Energie Atomique*, was created with a view to training specialists and developing new industrial techniques for the peaceful uses of nuclear energy— for France was not prepared to participate in the costly and frantic arms race which began as soon as the Iron Curtain had rung down. However, in latter years her rulers decided to follow the fashion, and by the time these lines appear in print she may have already tested some of her nuclear weapons in the Sahara desert.

France certainly has enough uranium for the purpose. In fact, she seemed to *reculer pour mieux sauter* by refraining from doing anything spectacular while quietly building up her research organization and her stocks of nuclear fuel. Intensive prospecting was undertaken in France as well as in French territories overseas, and very good deposits of pitchblende were found near Limoges. The Curies could have saved themselves the trouble of getting their uranium slag all the way from Bohemia!

The first five-year plan for the development of atomic energy began with the construction of a nuclear research centre on the plateau of Saclay, a dozen miles south of Paris. It has now a staff of 2000 people, including 500 engineers and scientists, and three piles, two using natural uranium and heavy water, and the third, which became critical in 1957, operating as a homogeneous plutonium pile.

Four other large reactors are already in use in other establishments—in Châtillon near Paris, where the first French experimental pile, Zoé, a heavy-water reactor, has been running since 1948, at the research centre at Grenoble, and at Marcoule, in the Rhône valley, the recently built headquarters of the industrial group, where two reactors, large graphite piles, are already in operation; a few more are in construction, mainly for the production of plutonium. Although French production of fissile uranium doubled in 1956–57, it was decided to concentrate more on plutonium within the framework of the second five-year plan from 1957 to 1961; the reasons are financial as well as technical, as the diffusion of U-235 is more expensive and complicated than the manufacture of plutonium once the reactors for this purpose are available.

All this is mainly preparatory work for the massive utilization of nuclear energy, which will make France the leading atomic nation on the European Continent this side of the Iron Curtain. The two completed Marcoule reactors—both fuelled with natural uranium and moderated by graphite, one air-cooled, the other carbon-dioxide-cooled—are already feeding 25,000 kw each into the national grid. But the generation of electricity on a larger scale will begin when France's first big commercial power station, in the lower Loire valley, starts up in 1959, feeding 60,000 kw into the grid. From then on up to 1965 France intends to open every eighteen months a new, more powerful and more effective power station. She has the fuel, she has the scientists and engineers, she has the technical knowledge, and she has tremendous enthusiasm and drive in her bid for atomic leadership in Europe. Needless to say that she has also advanced plans for building nuclear-powered ships and other means of transport, and that her radio-active isotopes industry, centred on Châtillon, strives hard to compete with Britain in the world market.

Europe's Small Nations

From the point of view of atomic development, the German Federal Republic is still a 'small nation'. Banned from undertaking nuclear research for ten years after the end of the Second World War, and forbidden to acquire fissile materials from abroad, Western Germany is now trying to make up for

96

An aerial view of Calder Hall, the world's first full-scale nuclear power station, comprising stations A and B. Each station consists of two reactors with their heat exchangers, a turbine hall and two cooling towers

No. 1 reactor of the Calder Hall A generating unit

A process worker
in a protective
'Windscale suit'
at Dounreay

Shippingport: America's first commercial nuclear power station. The tubing above the reactor contains automatic recording instruments

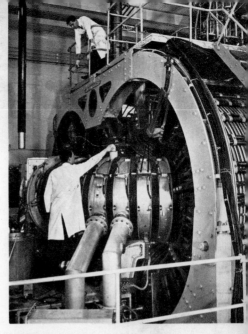

The Zero Energy Thermo-
nuclear Assembly, (ZETA),
at Harwell. The transformer
windings and the torus
(doughnut ring) can be seen

How the thermonuclear flame would look if one could see
inside the torus

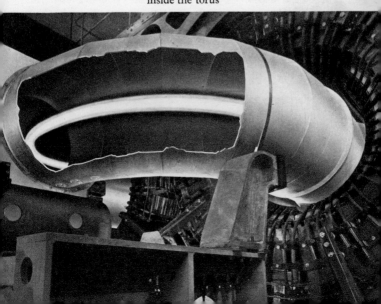

The six-million-volt
electrostatic generator
at Aldermaston,
Britain's nuclear
weapons centre

A concrete 'tunnel' under construction at the Brookhaven
National Laboratory, U.S.A., which will house the magnet for a
25,000-30,000 million electron volt proton-synchrotron

lost time. Research reactors are running, or nearing completion, in Munich, Berlin, Hamburg, Frankfurt, Karlsruhe and Cologne; the first four were bought in America, together with the fuel, U-235. The Berlin reactor is a homogeneous one, operating with boiling water, and producing about 50 kw.

Without nuclear energy, Germany, like Britain, would soon be faced with a serious fuel shortage. A Federal German 'Atomic Commission' is in charge of developments and says that it hopes to produce 500,000 to 900,000 kw by 1965, at about 2d. per kw. The Commission expects to obtain equipment from Britain, or build it in Germany under British licence. One of the reactors in construction, for instance, is of the DIDO type. The difficulty is that of getting nuclear fuel; the US Atomic Energy Commission has been unable to promise the release of U-235, and Britain has none to spare. Western Germany has, however, a few uranium deposits of her own which might help her to get started—provided she will not be forced to participate in the nuclear arms race, but will be allowed to do what her scientists can do best: research work.

The Karlsruhe reactor, the biggest research pile, is an entirely German construction; it runs on uranium from the Fichtel Mountains and heavy water from the Höchster Farbwerke, a famous chemical plant. The Hamburg reactor is a 'combined operation' of the four coastal *Länder* in northwest Germany; it will be mainly devoted to marine propulsion research. Research into thermo-nuclear fusion is being carried out by Dr Diebener in Hamburg, Professor Heisenberg in Göttingen, and Dr Kranz in Munich, where a 1,000-kw pool-type research reactor started up in 1958. It is the main tool of the new Max Planck Institute, which also has a strong ring-shaped magnetic accelerator.

Eastern Germany has two special reasons for embarking on a large-scale nuclear-power programme—it suffers from recurrent coal shortages, and it has big uranium resources. It is said that in these mines, which border on the Czech ones in the St Joachimsthal region, some 100,000 workers, including women, are employed under conditions amounting to forced labour; reports say that many are suffering from the effects of radiation because safety measures are poor. The country plans to build about twenty nuclear-power stations by 1970. So far one experimental reactor, designed and installed by

Russian engineers, is in operation in Eastern Germany's atomic-research centre at Rossendorf, just outside the Weisser Hirsch, a Dresden suburb; the centre's research director, Dr Manfred von Ardenne, is a leading German electronic and nuclear scientist who spent a number of years in the Soviet Union. He is responsible for the close co-ordination of his work with that of the Russians.

The Rossendorf reactor is of the LIDO ('swimming-pool') type, with a capacity of only 2000 kw, working with uranium 235, moderated and cooled by heavy water. It will be used for research and for the production of radio-isotopes.

The Netherlands, too, are an energy-hungry country. "It is a matter of life and death for us to build up an atomic industry", said Professor J. Milatz, director of the Netherlands Reactor Centre, in 1957. Holland's first power station is scheduled to start up in 1962, and half of her total electricity supply will come from atomic energy by 1975.

The Netherlands Reactor Centre at Arnhem is co-operating closely with the British Atomic Energy Authority. Its first experimental reactor began operating in the village of Petten, on the North Sea, in 1958; it is a high-flux type of reactor bought from America. A liquid-suspension, homogeneous type is being built at Arnhem, where a dry-suspension reactor will be the next project to be completed, and a boiling-water reactor is being developed at Halden in Norway under a joint scheme which the two countries began as far back as 1950.

This is one of the most interesting forms of international atomic co-operation. Norway's first experimental reactor was built at Kjeller, working with heavy water produced at the Norsk Hydro in Rjukan (see Chapter II); the plant re-started production in 1946, after the damage inflicted by the commandos during the war had been repaired. The uranium used at Kjeller was bought already before the war from a Dutch university. Future Dutch–Norwegian co-operation plans include marine propulsion development and further experiments with the SUSPOP reactor, which was one of the sensations of the 1955 International Conference on the Peaceful Uses of Atomic Energy in Geneva. It can burn minute grains of a compound of enriched uranium oxide fuel and beryllium oxide, each of which is about one-hundredth of an inch in diameter. These grains are forced through the reactor, where part of the uranium is fissioned to produce 1200° C of heat.

The burnt grains are then re-cycled by being pushed into a stream of helium gas, which carries them into the heat-exchanger and from there back into the pile.

Britain, too, takes part in the Dutch–Norwegian Halden reactor project. The British and Norwegian governments signed an agreement in summer, 1957, providing for the supply of the uranium fuel elements by Britain; in return, British scientists and engineers will benefit from the operating experience of the team at Halden. The reactor is designed to produce steam for wood-pulp mills and other industries.

Sweden also has a 100-kw heavy-water research reactor. Its name, somewhat out of tune with the wide-awake age of nuclear energy, is SLEEP (Swedish Low Energy Experimental Pile), and it has been built 100 ft under the old city of Stockholm. Sweden is now producing its own uranium. A private company has been given permission to build a 20,000-kw reactor, to be completed in 1959, in the south of Sweden; its output of steam, however—like the Halden plant in Norway—will not be used to produce electricity, but will be utilized directly in an adjoining paper-mill. A 100,000-kw power station is planned in the Bohuslan Province, but it may not be ready before 1965. Sweden, with nearly three times the territory of England and Wales but only 7 million inhabitants, is rich in hydro-electric power and has little need for additional energy.

Italy, with British help, is building a 200,000-kw power plant of the Calder Hall type near Latina, 50 miles south of Rome. The agreement between the two countries was the first of its kind, providing for extensive participation of British engineering firms. Switzerland, however, has already its own nuclear engineering concern with a team drawn from the leading companies of the country; within a few years, Switzerland—which has hardly any mineral fuel resources, though a good deal of hydro-electric power—will need nuclear energy for its rapidly expanding industry. Pilot plants for the production of heavy water and pilot reactors are already in operation. One, of the LIDO swimming-pool type, is a 'left-over' from the First International Conference on the Peaceful Uses of Atomic Energy, held in Geneva in 1955.

International Co-operation

That conference marked the beginning of a new era in the utilization of nuclear power. Held under the auspices of the

United Nations, it was mainly a scientific meeting of delegates from seventy-three countries, and its principal purpose was the exchange of information. Professor Dr Homi J. Bhabha, of India, was the president of the conference; one of its most important features was the attendance of scientists, engineers, and government officials from the Soviet Union and her allies. "Knowledge once given cannot be taken back," said Professor Bhabha, "and in organizing this conference the nations of the world have taken an irreversible step forward, a step from which there is no retreat."

All aspects of nuclear energy save the military one were discussed with surprising frankness, from the design of reactors to the problems of waste and public health. The world's probable power needs in 1975 and 2000 were the subject of a special study published in a paper which became the centre of interest among the delegates; it started out from the figures for 1952: 82 per cent of all useful energy was consumed in the 'developed' areas of the world, where consumption reached an average of 10,000 kw-hours per head as compared with only about 1000-kw-hours per head in the underdeveloped areas. The study anticipated rapid development in these areas of the world during the second half of our century, with these probable results:

Requirements of useful energy in million million kilowatt-hours in 1952, 1975, and 2000

	1952	1975	2000
Industry	5·8	18·0	60·0
Transport	0·8	2·5	8·0
Agriculture	0·3	0·5	1·0
Households	3·3	6·0	15·0
Total	10·2	27·0	84·0

This estimated increase seems fantastic; yet we have seen an even more fantastic growth in world production of energy in the last 100 years. In 1860 the total—comprising coal, lignite, oil, and water power—was the equivalent of just over 1 million million kw-h; by 1914 the figure had risen to 10 million million kw-h, and today it is 25 million million kw-h, also including natural gas (which was not utilized before the 1880s).

The Geneva Conference supplied the foundation of an international co-operation in the field of nuclear energy, without which there would be little chance of satisfying the world's power requirements in the future. "Most of the next decade," said Sir John Cockcroft at Geneva, "will be occupied in laying a sound basis from which nuclear power can expand rapidly to become in the end the major power source in the world." Professor Bhabha went even further when he said, "Atomic power definitely supposes an international society pledged to maintain peace; a major prerequisite is that the major nations should agree to maintain peace."

The practical development of these noble ideas has, in fact, made some progress. Already in 1953 President Eisenhower had suggested the formation of an International Atomic Energy Agency. It came into being in October, 1956, and has now over sixty member countries both in the West and the East. It held its first conference in Vienna in 1957, one of the very few international meetings at which the two opposing camps of our world showed themselves in complete agreement—or nearly so. The conference decided to adopt Vienna as the permanent seat of the IAEA; a Czechoslovak chairman and an American director-general were elected. The Soviet Union, the USA, and Portugal offered to contribute quantities of uranium to an international 'atom bank' for use in under-developed countries under the agency's auspices, and it was agreed to create a machinery for international control of nuclear technology 'with a view to excluding its abuse for military purposes'. One of the main activities of the agency is the study of radiation hazards and the suggestion of protective measures. The conference decided on a first annual budget of $4 million, one third to be contributed by America and 15 per cent by Russia. The IAEA will report on its first year's activities to the Second International Conference on the Peaceful Uses of Atomic Energy, to be held in Geneva in September, 1958, on the same lines as the first in 1955.

There are other international organizations for atomic co-operation. As long ago as 1949 the French nuclear physicist, Louis de Broglie, suggested that the European nations should form a council for promoting nuclear research. UNESCO took up the idea, and in 1952 the *Conseil Européen pour les Recherches Nucléaires* (CERN), the European Council for

Nuclear Research, was called into being. Twelve nations are members: Belgium, Denmark, France, Great Britain, Greece, Holland, Italy, Norway, Sweden, Switzerland, Western Germany, and Yugoslavia. Switzerland offered CERN a home in the form of a site at Meyrin, near the French border, where research laboratories are now being built. A very powerful proton-synchrotron will be completed by 1960. The cost of running CERN is borne by France and Britain with about 24 per cent each, Germany with 18 per cent, and the other countries with smaller contributions. The scientists who will be working with the proton-synchrotron and the other machines to be built for CERN are taking a hand in their design and construction. Team work is the over-riding rule in this organization. Special problems of nuclear research are dealt with at the University of Geneva by scientists from various member countries; theoretical work is being done at the universities of Edinburgh, Upsala and Copenhagen, while cosmic-ray research is carried out by a relay team on the ridge of the Jungfrau.

'Euratom', on the other hand, is the nuclear branch of the European Iron and Steel Community. The treaty of the 'European Atomic Energy Community' was signed in Rome by Western Europe's industrial nations—Belgium, France, Western Germany, Italy, Luxembourg, and the Netherlands— in March, 1957. Britain is not directly associated with Euratom, but its members are also members of the OEEC (Organization for European Economic Co-operation), and these two bodies are working closely together in yet another organization, the 'European Nuclear Energy Agency', of which Britain is also a member. The 'Three Wise Men' of Euratom, as they have been called—M. Armand of France, Professor Giodani of Italy, and Herr Etzel of Western Germany—have worked out a plan to instal 15 million kw of nuclear energy by 1967; by 1975 the Euratom target plan will save 100 million tons of coal a year and require about 5000 tons of uranium a year if plutonium recycling is by then in full operation. Another 5000 tons of uranium a year will be required for the initial fuel charges for about 5 million kw of new atomic-power stations per year. But by that time improvements in the 'neutron economy' of reactors—by the introduction of fast breeder reactors—may reduce fuel requirements considerably. The three wise men believe that

Europe's nuclear power will, from 1967, begin to oust American coal imports.

An establishment of immediate practical value is 'Euro-chemic', a factory for the processing of radio-active waste, set up by twelve Continental countries at Mol in Belgium in 1958. It is expected to turn 100 tons of waste annually into useful radio-isotope products.

International Competition

Atomic energy is being extensively used, or misused, in international business as well as in politics, quite apart from the nuclear-weapons issue. There is no doubt that atomic energy will yield enormous profits in the near future, and we can already see the manufacturing nations jockeying for position in the race for the world markets, especially in the under-developed areas. Both the USA and Britain are now in a position to sell power plants and technological know-how, and at present these two countries are the principal rivals in Europe. In Asia, however, they are both struggling hard against the third competitor, Russia. All three nations are exporting technologists, power-station designs, and actual reactors. Britain and America are both developing small atomic plants expected to produce energy for only 1–1½d. per kw-h, the American reactor using the pressurized-water system of heat transfer, the British one working with gas as a coolant; there is bound to be a good deal of fair or not-so-fair competition, especially in the Middle East. Here the Bagdad Pact has enabled Britain to keep her foot in the door; she offered the other Pact members—Persia, Iraq, Pakistan, and Turkey—the necessary help in running the nuclear training centre in Bagdad, established in 1957. Harwell-trained instructors are already passing their knowledge on to Middle Eastern students.

The Pacific, however, is America's theatre of operations. The USA Government has established a nuclear-research centre for the Colombo Pact countries in the Philippines, also with training as its main function. Atomic trade, we may well say today, will follow nuclear training.

In 1958 three groups of British firms were invited to tender for the construction of Japan's first great nuclear-power station with 150,000-kw capacity, to be built at Tokai, 65 miles north of Tokio. Japanese experts believe that the Calder

103

Hall type of power station could be reinforced to make it resistant to earthquakes.

In the Commonwealth, which comprises some under-developed areas, nuclear power plays a rapidly expanding part, although only Canada, India, and Australia have made an active start in reactor design and construction. India has great resources of hydro-electric power which are waiting to be exploited, but Indian experts are wondering whether nuclear-power stations will not be cheaper to build. The Indian Government is wisely sending great numbers of young scientists and technologists to Western countries (we do not know how many are going to Russia) to learn the essentials of nuclear-power production. Of all the under-developed countries, India—and probably South-East Asia—would benefit most from an extensive atomic-energy scheme, which, by raising living standards rapidly, would help to break down the old caste barriers and superstitions which have held in check the countries' great economic potential. Poverty, dirt, and disease are not only the effect of under-development—they are just as much its cause, and nuclear power may be the force that can break that vicious circle once for all.

For Australia atomic power means something very special. It means hope for the fulfilment of a national dream: that of making the arid, waterless inland bloom. Australian, British and American scientists have spoken of the possibility of distilling fresh water from sea-water at a cost of 5s. for 1 million gallons, and of irrigating the Australian desert with it. Chances are that, given water, Australia could in time produce more food than America. A ring of nuclear-power stations along the coast could do the job of distilling fresh water and pumping it into a network of canals. Australia has all the atomic fuel it would need for this gigantic task; substantial uranium deposits have been discovered in Queensland, in South Australia, and in the Northern Territory.

Reactors at Mount Gambier, South Australia, and Mount Isa, the silver-mining town in Queensland, are in course of construction. By 1965 nuclear power will also be needed for industry, although coal is still plentiful and many hydro-electric schemes can add to the continent's energy supply. But Australia's economy is expanding very fast.

Africa, too, has its great hydro-electric schemes: Aswan, the Owen Falls, the Kariba Gorge, the Volta scheme at the

Gold Coast, and several other major projects; nuclear power, therefore, will not play an important part in the near future, although no continent is richer in uranium than Africa. Thus it is bound to get its share of prosperity in the atomic age provided the white man can restrain his greed and decides to make the African his partner in the uranium business.

The Uranium Rush

South Africa's enormous wealth in atomic fuel became known very soon after the first bombs had dropped on Japan, and there was a 'uranium rush' comparable only to the gold rush in California 100 years earlier. Gold and uranium, in fact, seem to have some geological affinity; South Africa has an abundance of both, and today the Union is thriving on its uranium production at least as much as on its gold-digging.

The Belgian Congo is one of the oldest sources of pitch-blende for the production of radium, but recently many more parts of Africa have been found to contain uranium in one form or another. The United Kingdom Atomic Energy Authority has opened special offices in Salisbury, capital of the Federation of Rhodesia and Nyasaland, and in Dodoma, Tanganyika, for giving technical advice and help to prospectors in search of uranium ore. Mines are springing up at many places in these territories as well as in Kenya, Uganda, Swaziland, and British Guiana. The French, on the other hand, have discovered rich uranium deposits under the Sahara desert in Algeria—one more reason for their desperate attempt to hang on to that country, tooth and nail.

In 1942, when uranium was first required for the Manhattan Project, the Belgian Congo and the Eldorado area in Northern Canada were the only available sources. After the war many more deposits were found in Canada, especially in the Blind River district of Ontario. Most of Canada's uranium is sold to the USA; some—about £8 million worth per year—goes to Britain, and Western Germany has a ten-year agreement with Canada for the shipment of 100 tons of unprocessed ore a year. Japan buys an occasional five or ten tons for experimental purposes from Canada. The USA, too, have some uranium, mainly in South Dakota and the Colorado Plateau.

Australia is rich in uranium, and great discoveries were also made in New Zealand. France and Portugal, Sweden and the Fiji Islands are also important uranium producers outside the

Soviet orbit. Italy hopes to mine 350 tons by 1962: about 30 per cent of her requirements by that time. The total reserves of high-grade uranium concentrates outside Russia and her satellites has been estimated at over 1 million tons. But in addition there are tens of millions of tons of uranium contained in phosphates, shales, coals, lignites and granites; to extract the metal from these combinations is technically not too difficult, but rather costly, at least with present-day methods. It may be assumed that one 250,000th part of the entire earth crust consists of uranium in some combination, which means that it is as frequent as lead or zinc.

Russia says little about the size of her uranium deposits, the most important one seems to be in the Ferghana district in Siberia; but they may not be as large as those in the *Erzgebirge*, or Ore Mountains, in the border region between Eastern Germany and Bohemia—with St Joachimsthal-Jachymov as its main mining centre, the only one that came to the Curies' minds when they were looking for uranium in their search for the mysterious radio-active element in the pitchblende (see Chapter I). Here is one of the world's richest 'primary vein' deposits (primary ore minerals are pitchblende, uraninite, davidite, brannerite and coffinite, which all look like hard, grey-black stone, and contain up to 70 per cent uranium).

But we do not depend only on uranium as nuclear fuel. Thorium, as has been found out since the end of the war (see Chapter III), is also extremely useful for this purpose, and there is much more of it in the earth's crust than uranium. India, South Africa, West Africa and South America have rich deposits of sands containing thorium oxide. Besides, thorium occurs in about fifty minerals as chief constituent. (Its primary ore minerals are called monazite, thorite, thorianite and fergusonite.) The chief thorium deposits in the Soviet Union are in the Ural Mountains; there is also some in Korea, Indonesia, Malaya, Thailand, and Ceylon. Ton for ton, thorium can do just as much useful work in a thermal reactor as uranium.

Uranium and thorium prospecting is necessarily very different from searching for gold or diamonds. 'Wild-cat' prospecting—the way in which the gold-diggers made their fortune in the old days—has been superseded by scientific methods. Geological knowledge is essential, and so are recording instruments such as the Geiger counter (see Chapter

II). We are learning more and more about the distribution of nuclear raw material in the Earth, and many deposits have been found in places which the old-time geologist would have regarded as unlikely.

Geiger counters are today available in many varieties, from the light-weight portable type to one fixed to the top of a motor-car—which makes surveying possible at a speed of 30 mph if the area has a good network of roads—or suspended from the cabin of a helicopter flying at an altitude of about 500 ft. Other models are specially designed for 'geochemical prospecting' in areas where the uranium has 'migrated' with the ground-water, and for radiometric logging of boreholes.

Once the uranium has been found and the digging begun, the ore grade selector becomes one of the essential instruments: it is an arrangement of Geiger counters on a bridge-shaped frame under which the tubs with the mineral are made to pass. As the tubs roll on, the selector records whether their contents are above or below a given level.

The manufacture of uranium metal from the ore consists in crushing it and attacking it with mixed sulphuric and nitric acids. The solution is then filtered to remove impurities. The uranium is precipitated as a crude peroxide, which is again dissolved in nitric acid; after concentration by evaporation (to remove the remaining impurities) the uranium is made to combine with ammonia; it is then heated, treated with other acids and hydrogen, mixed with calcium chips in a refractory container, and finally 'fired'. The high temperature generated results in a 'billet' of uranium covered by slag. The billet is then cast into the required form.

This is a rather complicated and highly developed process, but it has proved economical and satisfactory. In the case of thorium processing is not yet as highly developed, but it is basically the same—after 'opening out' in acid and purification the result is a pure oxide, which is mixed with calcium and heated to produce a lime matrix containing beads of the thorium metal, Th-232. This is irradiated in a reactor and turns, via the unstable Th-233 produced by neutron capture, into the nuclear fuel uranium 233.

But the technologists have not had enough experience of working with thorium to decide whether as a nuclear raw material it has advantages compared with uranium.

At any rate, we have enough of both of these nuclear fuels

to solve all our energy problems this century, even without the utilization of thermo-nuclear energy. "Poverty, starvation, cold and discomfort will be things of the past," said Lord Chandos in 1956 in his presidential speech at the Manchester College of Science and Technology. "The only reason I mind being over 60 is that I shall not live to see this exhilarating age."

V

SORCERY WITH ISOTOPES

ONE OF the by-products of the discovery of radium was the salvation of the little town of St Joachimsthal from ruin and decay. Ten years after the Curies' achievement it had become the first radium spa in the world, with a large sanatorium visited by people suffering from skin and blood diseases, cancer, nervous complaints and rheumatism. For the people of St Joachimsthal it was a great satisfaction that what they had believed for centuries was now confirmed by modern Science. They had always been wearing small pieces of uranium ore on strings around their necks as amulets, convinced of the magic healing power of those chips of black mineral. The local baker went one better: while the sanatorium was still in course of erection he collected water from the mine (presumably slightly radio-active), put it in his large kneading-trough, and invited people to take a bath in it. He did roaring business.

The baker of St Joachimsthal was the first to use the power of radio-active isotopes for medicinal purposes. More than fifty years later, Dr W. E. Libby, of the US Atomic Energy Commission, said at the Geneva Conference of 1955, "Isotopes in themselves justify all that we have done in the development of nuclear energy."

The story of the utilization of radio-isotopes is indeed a remarkable one. Before 1947 scientists were merely speculating on the potential good they might do in this or that field. In September of that year a little package left the laboratories at Oak Ridge, Tennessee, on its way to the airport and to Australia: the first consignment of a few grams of radio-active material for medical research.

Today it is estimated that radio-isotopes are saving more than $400 million a year in America's industry alone.

In 1948 two private houses which had been taken over by the British Atomic Energy Authority near the town of Amersham in Buckinghamshire were converted into an isotope factory.

Today Britain exports more radio-isotopes than any other country; it delivers them to more than sixty countries on every continent.

How Elements are 'Cooked'

We know that every element exists in a number of forms, chemically indistinguishable, but differing in atomic weight. Chemically, the behaviour of heavy hydrogen is similar to that of ordinary hydrogen, and that of uranium 238 similar to that of its lighter radio-active twin U-235. The only difference is that the isotope, the twin, has more or less neutrons, electrically neutral particles, in its nucleus than its 'normal' brother; its atomic weight is therefore different. Some isotopes are radio-active because they are unstable: their nuclei are continually breaking up, particles are flying off in all directions, electrons are 'liberated' and shoot into space. As these atoms decay they change into atoms of other elements —we know that the difference between one element and another is the number of particles that make up its nucleus and the corresponding number of electrons.

The radio-activity of such an isotope becomes less and less as the number of its remaining atoms falls; the rate of decay is unaffected by temperature, pressure, or other outward conditions, and its radiation cannot be made to cease. We measure its 'useful age' by its half-life, that is, the time taken for the radio-activity to be reduced to one half. That half-life may be anything from a fraction of a second to millions of years—according to the nature of the element.

Radiation is generally of three types: alpha particles, which are in fact helium nuclei (a close combination of two neutrons and two protons, but without their electrons and therefore positively charged)—they are heavy high-speed particles which can easily be stopped by a thin piece of matter such as a sheet of paper; beta particles, which are high-speed electrons of almost no weight—they can be stopped by several feet of air or a fraction of an inch of metal; and gamma radiation, which is an electro-magnetic radiation similar to X-rays, light rays, or radio waves—it can be stopped only by very thick metal, brick, or concrete shields.

Some radio-isotopes, like U-235, occur in Nature. But scientists have found that a large number of artificial radio-iso-topes can be produced by 'cooking' their normal twins in a

110

nuclear reactor. The serious danger of radio-activity, that it is 'infectious', is at the same time its great boon; by bombarding stable materials with neutrons in a reactor you can make the nuclei break up, to become unstable. This is how the transmutation of elements works: if you knock a beta particle, an electron, off the nucleus of an atom you shift it one place to the right in the Periodic Table, the list of elements according to their atomic numbers—nitrogen, atomic number 7, becomes oxygen, atomic number 8; if you knock off an alpha particle (2 protons + 2 neutrons) you shift it two places to the left —thallium (81) would then turn to gold (79), or iodine (53) to antimony (51). But if you knock off 2 beta particles and 1 alpha particle, it will remain in the same place in the Periodic Table, yet become a new form of the original element: in other words, an isotope of the original element, but with different atomic weight because it has different mass. Stable elements can be turned into unstable, radio-active isotopes by neutron bombardment. But we do not yet fully understand the reason why so many isotopes continue of their own account the breaking-up process once the neutrons coming from outside have started it.

Our working knowledge and experience with these 'cooked' elements, however, enables us to use them in so many different ways that their value, even after a mere ten or twelve years of practice, borders on the miraculous.

The Case of the Siamese Twins

One day in 1955 two unfortunate children were brought to London from West Africa: Siamese twins. Their mother, desperately worried, consulted a famous British surgeon. Was there any chance of separating them? What was the risk?

Only a few years earlier the surgeon would have shrugged his shoulders. He could only have guessed how the bloodstream circulated in these two little bodies. But now he had an instrument that would tell him exactly how much the blood was shared between the two. Nuclear science had given him the radio-active isotope.

A minute quantity of radio-active phosphorus was injected into the twins' bloodstream, and its progress traced with Geiger counters. As a result, the surgeon could tell the mother exactly what the risk of a separating operation was: one baby would live; the other might die.

111

Today Baby Boko is a healthy, normal West African child. It may never know that it was once part of a double-headed monster. Without the information gained from the radio-isotope, the surgeon might have refused to operate because the risk of killing both children would have been too great. Instead of growing up as half a freak, useless for ordinary life, Boko can lead a normal existence, romping and playing with other children.

There is hardly any hospital in the world which has no use for radio-isotopes. They are applied in diagnosis, treatment and research. In diagnosis, the tracer technique can tell the doctor a great deal about the working of his patient's body. For instance, the behaviour of the thyroid gland—which controls metabolism and mental activity—is studied with the help of radio-iodine. Water containing this isotope in very small quantities is drunk by the patient, and a Geiger counter held close to his neck records the rate at which the iodine is being absorbed by the gland. Even the shape of the gland can be mapped out by tracing its radio-activity.

The question may be asked whether for this latter purpose X-rays may not be more suitable and reliable. The fact is that X-rays, much like gamma rays, are much more dangerous to the human body than cautiously dosed radio-isotopes. Besides, X-ray equipment is rather expensive and cumbersome. Radio-isotopes, on the other hand, need no apparatus, they can be carried about easily, no power supply and no maintenance are necessary. Since radio-active isotopes of an element behave biochemically just like its ordinary stable atoms, there is no risk of any dangerous or unpleasant chemical reaction. For instance, radio-phosphorus can safely be used to check one of the most delicate processes in surgery, the assimilation of skin grafts; or radio-iodinated human serum albumin can be used to measure blood volume, to investigate disorders of the circulatory system, and possibly locate brain tumours, while a radio-active form of common salt helps to measure the blood circulation in limbs.

The unique value of the tracer technique lies in the fact that these isotopes provide the doctor with the ability to follow a specific batch of atoms through a complicated system such as the human body, regardless of all the other atoms present and of all the biochemical processes that are going on in the organism.

After diagnosis comes treatment. Here again radio-isotopes

have taken over from X-rays in many fields of medicine. Tissue-destroying gamma-rays, electro-magnetic waves of a shorter length than X-rays but of very similar properties, are emitted by radium and a number of isotopes. Rapidly dividing tissues such as those of cancerous growths and malignant tumours are particularly liable to be destroyed by radiation.

There are three ways in which radio-isotopes can be used for this kind of treatment: by radiation from an external source similar to X-ray treatment; by implanting a radiation source in the patient's body in the form of needles, little capsules, or 'seeds'; and by passing a solution of radio-active salts into a bladder or sac which is placed at the site of the growth.

Artificial radio-isotopes are much cheaper than radium, which until the end of the Second World War was the main source of natural radio-activity in medicine. They have also the great advantage of being available in such a variety that the most suitable kind of radiation can be applied in every individual case, and that some can be chosen according to their half-life, so that removal of seeds after treatment is unnecessary —they have done their work and spent their useful energy, and they cannot do any harm if left where they are.

Cobalt v Cancer

Perhaps the most effective instrument in the fight against cancer is cobalt 60. Produced, in Britain, by Harwell's DIDO reactor, radio-active cobalt is so powerful that one third of a cubic inch has a radiation content of 340 curies, more than that of all the therapeutic radium sources in Britain put together. It is enclosed in a large, globe-like apparatus 2 ft in diameter, containing two tons of lead as a biological shield. The lead can be moved to open a tiny window for the gamma rays of the cobalt morsel, about equal to an X-ray beam of 3 million volts. A flick of the operator's finger, and the lead diaphragm alters its shape according to what the doctor wants the patient to receive in the way of therapeutic radiation. The cobalt beam can be pin-pointed to treat even the smallest area.

Canada was the first country to experiment with cobalt 60. There are more cobalt deposits in that country than in any other part of the world; the metal, which belongs to the iron group of elements, even gave its name to the town of Cobalt, Ontario, 330 miles north of Toronto, where the greatest deposits ever to be found were discovered at the beginning of this century. The metal is whitish and looks like nickel; but as soon as a little cobalt salt is added to potash glass the compound shows the brilliant bluish colour which we associate with the name of cobalt. It has been used in ceramic and paint manufacture for a long time, and 18th-century spies made invisible ink from it: the writing, unseen when done in a cobalt-chloride solution, becomes bright blue when the paper is heated. Canadian nuclear scientists, experimenting with cobalt isotopes, realized that they were holding in their hands an entirely new weapon against cancer because of the extremely strong gamma radiation emitted by the isotope cobalt 60. In due course, cobalt radiation will be stepped up to even greater intensity; a unit of 2000 curies will soon be in operation, and Britain's Wantage Radiation Laboratory, which belongs to the Atomic Energy Authority, is equipped with radio-cobalt sources of 10,000 curies. It will eventually have cobalt sources of half a million curies.

Another most important isotope for treatment of deep-seated cancer is cæsium. It is extracted from the radio-active waste products from uranium rods spent in thermal and other reactors. They are a kind of nuclear ash, whose utilization was achieved for the first time only in 1956, when a small piece of cæsium salt, about the size of four lumps of sugar, was concentrated by British radio-chemical scientists from highly active liquid waste. The piece, which was found to have a gamma-ray activity of more than 1200 curies, was melted at red heat into a platinum capsule, which in turn was set in an apparatus similar to that for cobalt treatment; but it has a novel type of shutter composed of curved plates of tungsten alloy moving round the surface of a sphere.

Twenty British hospitals are already working, or shortly expecting to work, with radio-cæsium. The treatment unit is protected by uranium shielding, and both sides of the patient can be seen during operation: one by direct view through a window, and the other by means of a closed-circuit television camera set up on the far side of the room, which must not be entered by hospital staff as long as the shutter releasing the gamma-rays is open. Radio-cæsium has an active life of thirty years.

Radio-iodine, which is so useful in tracing the activities of the thyroid gland, can also be used for treating the same organ. For this purpose it is taken internally as a salt in water; it will find its way rapidly to the gland. There is a short-lived isotope of iodine, with only 2·4 hrs' half life; it is a daughter element of the metal, tellurium (half-life, 3·2 days), from which it can be easily extracted in gaseous form and dissolved for injection into the patient; therefore radio-active tellurium is sent to the hospital, and the resident chemist will then produce from it the iodine isotope just before it is required.

Gold 198 is an isotope which is readily accepted by the body and used for injection into its cavities. As it has the form of a fine suspension, the particles will be distributed over very large surfaces, for instance of the lung or the bowels, and by their radiation help to stop the exudation of water which normally takes place in these organs, and which can accumulate to a dangerous degree in cases of illness. Radio-gold has also been used in a rubber catheter (a very thin tube), which is passed up an arm vein, right through the heart, and into the cancerous area of a lung!

Among the beta-ray sources, strontium 90 plays an important part. It can be used to remove malignant or scar tissue from the skin and even from such a delicate organ as the eye. Radio-phosphorus facilitates the scrutiny of nucleic acids, which in recent years have been found to play a vital role in cellular processes, especially in cell division and multiplication, while radio-sulphur helps to investigate the functioning of the process by which our bodies produce those gluey substances which lubricate our joints. Ordinary sulphur can be found in a certain type of white blood cell, and a special technique—called auto-radiography—has been developed to trace it: a shot of radio-sulphur is given to the patient or animal to be examined, and some blood cells are taken from him; they are laid directly on the photographic emulsion, which is blackened by the sulphur 35 emanation.

Other isotopes are used to study the importance of various elements in the food of a patient; the rate of elimination of certain substances from the body can be measured, and the rate of flow in blood and lymph-carrying organs, the total blood volume, even the rate of respiration can be determined with the help of isotopes.

'Labelling' Cells

Blood diseases such as anæmia are being examined with the help of radio-isotopes. It has been known for some time that the red cells of our blood normally live only about 120 days. Red cells can be 'labelled' with isotopes of carbon, nitrogen, or iron, but most effectively with chromium, with which the red cells combine readily. This is done by taking from the patient some blood and leaving it in a solution of chromium salt for an hour or so before re-injecting it into his bloodstream. Thus it can be determined how long the cells survive. In cases of severe shock, when transfusion is necessary—for instance, after an accident—this information may be of extreme importance.

It would take a good deal of space only to enumerate the steadily increasing number of applications of radio-isotopes in medicine. Carbon 14, isotopes of sodium, potassium, and chlorine, even of copper—they have all found a variety of uses, from determining the chemical processes in rheumatoid arthritis to helping in the treatment of liver and brain diseases. Naturally, the dangers of radiation occupy a large sector of medical work with isotopes. It appears that there is little permanency of radio-active substances in cells and body liquids, but the greatest hazard to men and animals comes from their retention in the bones. Breeding investigations with mice have shown that radio-active calcium which settles in the skeleton of the animal will decay by only 35–40 per cent in one year. When such a female mouse produces offspring with a completely normal father, the young mice will retain for a lifetime about half of the radio-activity present at birth. Some workers say that up to eleven generations are required before most of the radio-calcium atoms have disappeared, and there is no reason why things should be different in men and women.

Radiation can kill bacteria and other microscopic organisms. Anything used in medical practice can therefore be sterilized with isotopes; even experiments to sterilize hospital blankets, sutures and bandages have proved successful. In the treatment of antibiotics, radiation may also be of great importance. It causes a temperature rise of only 1–2° C, yet can reduce the bacteria in heat-sensitive antibiotics very effectively; this is easily achieved by short spells of isotope radiation. It might also be used in the final packaging of drugs without reducing their potency; penicillin, streptomycin and similar antibiotics have already been treated in this way. With all heat-sensitive drugs, isotope irradiation is the only possible method of purifying them almost 100 per cent even if the aseptic conditions under which they are now manufactured are relaxed—which would make production a great deal cheaper. They can be irradiated after they have been sealed in glass or plastic containers.

In 1958 America opened its first big atomic medical centre at Brookhaven, 70 miles from New York on Long Island. It has its own nuclear reactor specially designed for research and treatment; there are forty-eight rooms for hospital patients and laboratories for research in medical physics, pathology, microbiology, biochemistry, physiology, and industrial medicine. Apart from the 'cooking' of isotopes the reactor can, for instance, treat brain tumours by directing a neutron beam against the growth, which has first been localised by boron injected into the patient's bloodstream.

Bone grafts and arteries used in surgical transplantation are similarly heat-sensitive so that normal methods of sterilising them cannot be applied, and many surgeons now insist on isotope irradiation. It is equally effective with surgical instruments such as hypodermic needles, whose sterility can be improved after they have been sealed in their containers.

The Lifespan of a Sausage

America, where the daily waste of food reaches fantastic proportions, has spent millions of dollars on food-preservation research. Today scientists agree that with a great many foodstuffs isotope irradiation—for instance, with radio-cæsium—is the most effective and economical way of extending their storage 'lifespan'. In the case of sausages, ham, and bacon, storage life can be lengthened four or five times; it could be increased still more by bigger radiation doses, but there would be unpleasant side effects, such as deterioration of taste and flavour. There is, however, no danger of any harm to the consumer. The latest food-preservation technique is a combination of light cooking of the food and irradiation. Sometimes an antibiotic may be added as well.

We are only at the beginning of what is called 'bulk irradiation'. Radio-active isotopes can be used for the destruction of bacteria in foodstuffs by the ton. The storage life of meat carcases can be increased by gamma irradiation. But no less important is the ability of the gamma rays to 'inactivate' organic matter—to prevent, for instance, the sprouting

117

of potatoes during storage, which can be achieved by a very low dose of irradiation. This is an important factor in extending the marketing areas of seed potatoes to such places as South Africa and Australia because the potatoes which have to pass through tropical zones on their way to these areas are apt to sprout prematurely as the temperature rises. But the technique is not yet perfected; cobalt 60-irradiated potatoes were found to become shrivelled and taste sweet.

Insects are Man's implacable enemies, and here again isotopes are of great help. Bulk radiation of grain with gamma rays kills off grain beetles, weevils, and other insects which are so destructive in warm and humid climates. This, however, needs a larger dose than the inactivation of potatoes, but irradiation can be carried out while the grain is handled at the ports, and the incorporation of radiation sources in port installations would not cost too much. Most important is the sterilization of insect eggs, which does not require very long spells of irradiation. At the Geneva Conference of 1955 some spectacular results in this field were discussed, such as the elimination of the screw worm by the irradiation of the male flies.

The United Kingdom Atomic Energy Authority has set up its own 'animal farm' to test radiation-treated food. Here, rats, monkeys, and an occasional human volunteer are fed with irradiated foodstuffs, including packaged products such as spices and dried fruit, to discover whether they are in any way harmful. The American army also carries out such tests with human volunteers.

Indeed, agriculture will soon benefit enormously from isotope radiation. All over the world experimental work is going on with a view to producing improved strains of plants by systematic mutation. This is not a new idea; between the two World Wars the German geneticist Professor H. J. Müller used X-rays to study the mutations caused by gamma radiation in the fruit fly, drosophila, which reproduces rapidly so that successive generations can be observed within a short time. Today, isotopes have taken over from the cumbersome and expensive X-ray apparatus.

Britain, America, India and Sweden are the pioneer countries in this field. "Most agricultural species, even high-bred ones like barley, wheat, or corn, are still rather old-fashioned," said the Swedish research worker, Professor L.

Ehrenberg. "They have to be reconstructed for the requirements of modern agriculture, facilitating intensive mechanization and fertilizing of the soil."

Until now we have depended on the mutations—hereditary variations in plants and animals—caused by natural radioactivity in the ground and by cosmic rays. By irradiating seed or pollen or eggs it is possible to increase the number of mutations a hundred times; the changes are of much the same nature as the natural ones, and in both cases the proportion of 'useful' varieties is extremely small—no more than about one in a thousand.

Evolution Made to Order

This figure sounds modest, but we must remember that all living organisms, from moss to Man, have developed by way of these very rare, 'useful' mutations—first by natural selection, by the 'survival of the fittest', and later through selection by Man himself, who improved his crops and livestock by systematic cultivation and breeding. But while for hundreds of millions of years there were only the weak accidental radiation from the soil and the 'lucky hit' by some cosmic-ray particle causing these mutational improvements and developments, we have now, for the first time, a practical means of producing a new evolution 'to order'.

What does the radiation from an isotope do to seeds or eggs? It 'disturbs' the genes, the units of heredity, and the chromosomes, the carriers of hereditary characteristics—biologists have not yet been able to agree on the precise role which Nature has allotted to these two components of the living cell. Neither do we know completely what kind of 'disturbance' the gamma rays create in the cell; all we know is that isotope radiation, like X-rays, causes hereditary variations. Most of the changed characteristics seem to be controlled by only a few genes of relatively large effect, while the quantitative variations, such as those concerning yield and size, are determined by a large number of genes of individually small effect. Beyond that all is still guesswork.

All the more impressive is the list of what has already been achieved; here is a short selection. The first new strain produced by irradiation in America was a bush type of bean derived from a vine type. Seeds were treated with X-rays in 1941, and in recent years with isotopes; the result is a strain which can withstand wet weather, is resistant to disease and rotting, and is suitable for mechanical harvesting. The first large quantity of seeds was released for the 1957 crop season.

Also in America, extensive work with peanuts has shown that irradiation can develop strains with much higher yields. In Sweden an improved variety of white mustard of greater yield and oil content has been developed; also a more uniformly ripening, early, high-yielding variety of summer oil rape; and one of cooking pea, with higher yield, which is now being grown by the farmers. From the economic point of view it is significant that the annual government allocation for all mutation research work in Sweden is less than 250,000 crowns, while the new white mustard crop alone is estimated to represent a value of 2 million crowns per year!

Many countries are testing new varieties of wheat, barley, oats, soyabean, flax and other crops obtained by irradiation. Improvements already achieved are short and stiff-strawed types of cereals, weather-resistant, better able to make use of fertilizers, and better adapted to mechanical harvesting; types with shorter maturing periods and improved adaptation to varying rain periods. Japan is studying the possibility of improving its rice by irradiation. Germany is concentrating on horticultural mutations, and many other countries have started irradiation programmes with certain purposes in mind—Holland, Norway, Belgium, France and Finland, apart from the countries already mentioned. Those purposes may range from the attempt to achieve cross strains from normally incompatible parents by irradiating the pollen of one strain to that of breaking the close association of favourable and unfavourable characteristics which have hitherto been regarded as inseparable—oats, for instance, is resistant to one plant disease while being susceptible to another. That association has already been broken in radiation experiments, so that a new resistant strain can be developed.

The Russians, after the unfortunate Lysenko period when the official line was that 'Western genetics is bunk', have resumed their work with radio-isotopes in plant breeding. As long ago as 1947 they succeeded in increasing the yield, accelerating the blossoming and ripening and increasing the carbo-hydrates content of a number of plants, starting with rubber plants and sugar beets.

Britain—where the work is mainly done at the Wantage

Radiation Laboratory—hopes to complete the first phase of her extensive plant-breeding research programme by 1960. Here the emphasis lies to a large extent on developing pest-proof strains.

What the isotope does for agriculture is, therefore, that it enables Man to take a hand in directing evolution in his own way, and speeding it up enormously. Irradiation is a relatively simple and cheap means of greatly expanding the number of varieties available to the plant breeder for selection. So far very little work in this vein has been done with animals; but this, no doubt, will rank prominently on the research agenda once our scientists have discovered *what* they are actually doing when they irradiate the genes and chromosomes of living organisms. Beyond that there is the rather frightening aspect of selective breeding of humans by guided irradiation.

Isotopes in Industry

There is hardly any branch in industry which is not yet making use of radio-isotopes or will do so in the near future. The US oil industry alone estimates that its savings from the use of isotopes now amount to $180–200 million per year; this includes oil-well stimulation and logging, petroleum refining and pipeline oil-flow. The tracer technique is, for instance, extensively used in drilling and production operations. A cheap method for continuously determining sulphur and lead contaminants in oil processing is the measuring of the absorption of a certain type of radiation by the contaminants. On the other hand, radiation promotes chemical reactions, and here it plays already quite an important part in oil production as well as in other branches of industry.

In cable-making, for instance, certain physical changes which radiation can produce are put to very good use. Polyethylene, the plastic insulator, can be cross-linked by radiation, and the resulting polymer can stand up to much higher temperatures (150° C; ordinary polyethylene melts at 110° C). The vulcanization of rubber is usually carried out by using sulphur as the link between different atoms; by using radiation, however, rubber can be vulcanized without sulphur. Tyres made of radiation-vulcanized rubber are claimed to last longer because they are free of sulphur, and therefore of better temperature resistance.

The entire plastics industry is full of new or potential

customers for the isotope-producing establishments. A number of reactions can be triggered off by radiation: one active molecule causes the reaction of a number of inactive ones. What does this mean in practical terms? The plastic polythene, which is used for innumerable household articles, is normally manufactured under a pressure of over 1,000 atmospheres and at temperatures around 200° C. When radiation is used to start the initial reaction, polymerization—the forming of larger molecules or molecule 'chains' into new compounds—can be carried out at almost normal pressure and temperature, and the resulting plastic material is rather tougher than that produced by the conventional process! When non-irradiated polythene is melted it becomes a viscous liquid, while the irradiated material is transformed into a rubber-like mass which recovers its shape and hardens again on cooling. Many new applications are being discovered for this new material, irradiated polythene, with its great advantages, including increased strength, crack resistance, better elastic recovery, reduced creep under load and so on. It is preferred in wiring complicated electrical circuits, as it will not melt during soldering, and it is extensively used as a packing material because it can easily be heat-sealed. When uncooked food is enclosed in a polythene bag and then immersed in boiling water it will be cooked and sterilized at the same time; it can then be kept for long periods and removed from its bag only immediately before use: this new 'canning' technique is quite suitable for the home and can be done by the housewife without any special equipment.

It has long been realized that the various materials we are using today are at least 100 times weaker than their theoretical maximum strength, which can be calculated from inter-atomic forces. Within the next twenty years we shall progress quickly along the way to that optimum strength as we learn more and more about crystal structure and about the underlying reasons for material fatigue, which is now such a limiting factor in designing new machines, buildings, vehicles and other equipment for our daily lives and for industry; and we shall be able to produce materials with better magnetic and electric properties. In other words, we shall be in a position to fabricate materials to order for any special purpose, instead of making do with natural raw materials, as we have done for thousands of years.

Here, radiation by isotopes—'waste products' of atomic energy—will play a major part. Fantastic amounts of gamma-radiating sources will be available to us in years to come, and as their quantity grows their price will go down rapidly. Something like 2 per cent of the power of a nuclear station could be made available for this purpose, and this will doubtless become a matter of course in future power-station design. Cæsium 137 and cobalt 60 are likely to rank foremost among the possible radiation sources for industrial use; it is thought that they will be among the cheapest isotopes in the late 1960s.

One of the most conservative industries, building, will benefit enormously once it has made up its mind to work with new materials. Irradiated plastic sheets and other structural units have greater strength and elasticity than ordinary structural steel of the same thickness; besides, they are so heat-resistant that they will substantially reduce the risk of fire in buildings. They can be made either opaque or transparent. Owing to their great strength, however, they will have to be given their final form before irradiation, which means that conventional building practice will have to be reversed to some extent, and pre-fabrication will become the rule rather than the exception.

In the electronics industry, transistors are already ousting the radio valve (amplifier or thermionic valve) in countless pieces of equipment, from hearing aids to computers. Transistors are made of silicon or germanium crystals, and it has been found that irradiation can improve their properties to a great extent. This is of special value in high-speed circuits such as those used in electronic computers.

Looking into Cigarette Packets

Radio-isotopes have already found a very large number of uses as checking and measuring tools in industry. The cigarette which you are smoking, the foil and the carton of the packet may have been tested with radio-activity. For this purpose, beta particles—fast electrons which pass through a few feet of air and thin sheets of paper or metal—are the most suitable type of radiation; in passing through a thickness of material the number of beta particles in a beam is steadily reduced—as some of them are absorbed, and the amount of radiation that gets through indicates the thickness. A simple arrangement of a radiation source on one side of a moving belt with the packets on it and a detector—an adaptation of the Geiger counter—on the other side carries out a continuous automatic control of the cigarettes and shows how tightly the tobacco is packed. A 'feed-back' device, as used in all automation systems, adjusts the packing to the right level if the beta rays have found any fault with it.

Packages of detergents, cocoa tins, matchboxes, and a thousand other containers are checked by the same method; the beam penetrates through the top of the package as it passes, and if it is not properly filled it is thrown out automatically. The control of liquids in tins or bottles works on the same principle.

'Package monitoring' as an industrial operation is nothing new, but so far it has mainly been done with X-ray or ultrasonic equipment; both types are rather expensive and bulkier than isotope apparatus. But isotopes as measuring instruments or gauges are even more important in our highly automatized industries. They can find the thickness of a material in continuous production—metal sheeting, paper, plastics, rubber, etc.—without any physical contact with the material. Here again the radiation source is placed on one side of the moving material, often in the form of a tube extending over the whole width of the machinery, and the detector on the other. The greater the thickness of the material, the more radiation it absorbs, and the less falls on the detector. Very substantial savings in industry have already been achieved in this way. The detector is, of course, connected with a feed-back device for continuous adjustment of the thickness of the material while in production.

Another thickness gauge is based on the reflection or 'back-scattering' of beta particles. The proportion of electrons scattered by a thin sheet depends on its thickness and its atomic number. Thus, the thickness of, say, a coat of tin, zinc, paint, or other material on the surface of steel or plastic can be determined from the proportion of radiation 'back-scattered' as compared with reflection from a bare, uncoated steel or plastic surface. In other cases only one side of the material whose thickness is to be measured may be accessible; here again the back-scattering technique can be used for measuring thicknesses up to 1 in. of steel.

This method has also been developed for checking internal corrosion in the pipes and tanks of an oil refinery, and oil pipes can be checked in this way while they are in the ground. The technique consists in using the circumstance that the reflected waves have a different wave-length from the original beam, and by arranging that the detector is sensitive only to the reflected waves one can dispense with all shielding and give the instrument a small and handy form. This application of radio-isotopes is of great importance in industrial plants which formerly had to shut down their production process to have their pipelines etc. checked for corrosion. Now it can be done while the plant is in full operation.

Gamma rays, too, are scattered by matter; they are frequently used to measure the thickness of hot rolled steel strip and the wall thickness of closed tubes and tanks from the outside. In 1958, gamma rays from sodium 24 were made to produce a radiograph of a fallen trilithon at Stonehenge to find out if it was cracked right through. Only then did the engineers decide on the best way to lift the stone back to its original upright position.

A production problem which the layman rarely realizes is that of static electricity in synthetic fibre production. During their passage through the loom the fibres become electrified and begin to attract dust particles by their static charge; the result is a dirty product. By passing the fibres under a source of beta radiation the electric charge is removed and a much cleaner product obtained. The same technique is applied to the handling of very thin sheets of plastic material used for covering foodstuffs, etc., and in the manufacture of laminated glass.

Radiography with Thulium

There are so many industrial applications of radio-isotopes that one can mention only a few examples to show their astonishing variety. Previously the measuring of the rate of wear to which bearing surfaces are subjected used to take many hundreds of hours' running; but by making the bearing surfaces radio-active the rate of wear can be determined within a few minutes merely by measuring the growth of radio-activity in the lubricant. The point of leakage in a buried oil- or water-pipe can be found by pumping a weak radio-active solution through the pipeline under pressure; some of it will seep out of the leak and become absorbed in the surrounding soil. The radio-active solution is followed by clear water or

125

oil which flushes out the pipeline and also drives a self-contained detector attached to a miniature recording mechanism at a steady rate along the inside of the pipe. At the end of the pipeline the recording gear is removed and 'played back', indicating accurately the points of radiation—which are the leakage points. Alternatively, Geiger counters can be used above ground to find the leakage points. In the past large pasture areas have been polluted from oil seepage before the leaks were discovered.

A very simple method of measuring the level of a liquid in a closed vessel is the using of a little 'float' containing a radio-active source. This can be done even at extreme temperatures, with highly corrosive materials, or in other circumstances where conventional gauging methods would be unsuitable.

Radio-active isotopes can be used to check the effectiveness of mixing of a few ounces of some ingredient in tons of some bulk material. The ingredient is 'labelled' with the isotope before the mixing process begins; if the distribution is homogeneous the end product will show a stable level of radio-activity. An example of this is the manufacture of cattle food to which small quantities of vitamins have to be added. Before the introduction of radio-isotopes no manufacturer was able to guarantee that each sack of food contained exactly the right amount of vitamins. Incidentally, the type of isotope chosen for such purposes has a very short half-life, and its quantity is so small that the food will be completely free of radio-activity by the time it reaches the consumer.

In the motor industry small quantities of metals are now being measured with the help of isotopes. If a radio-active piston ring is used the wear of an internal-combustion engine can be investigated by measuring the radio-active debris carried away by the lubricating oil; this method is much more accurate and quicker than the older ones.

The safety of aircraft can be checked by adding small amounts of radio-active material to the fuel in order to find out if any spilling or leaking occurs, which may lead to a fire or an explosion.

X-rays are being superseded by radio-isotopes in many industrial processes. A relatively cheap radio-active source emitting gamma rays and weighing only an ounce or two can do the same job as an expensive X-ray apparatus. Radio-active thulium is the most efficient isotope for this purpose; its

126

gamma rays are about as penetrating as the X-rays from an average-size tube; they can be screened so thoroughly with lead that quite a strong source may be safely carried in a jacket pocket. Cobalt, too, is very efficient in cases where even stronger radiation is required. It may be used where routine checks of steel castings up to 6 in. thick have to be made to detect flaws or air bubbles. Cæsium, too, can be useful in revealing potentially dangerous porosities, cracks, and impurities in castings, forgings, and large-scale welds.

The extent to which isotopes can be used instead of the more expensive, complicated, bulky, and less manœuvrable X-ray apparatus (which requires high-voltage current for its operation) becomes increasingly apparent in various ways. Quite good radiographs of a man's hand can be obtained in less than a minute with radio-thulium. This may be extremely important in the case of accidents in places where hospitals equipped with X-rays are rare. Just like X-rays, isotope radiation produces pictures on photographic film; for the continuous examination of moving objects such as machinery in operation, the film can be replaced by a fluorescent screen. This technique is called gamma-ray fluoroscopy; it requires, however, a strong source of radiation. Another recently developed technique is that of xero-radiography, in which the film or screen is replaced by a polarized plate which displays an image without the need for photographic developing.

Pebbles with Holes

One day in 1956 2 lb of powdered glass were deposited in the Thames Estuary by workers of the Hydraulics Research Station under the auspices of the Port of London Authority. The glass had been made radio-active. For six months its movements with the mud on the river-bed were traced over 20 miles of the Thames; the results are being used as a guide in dredging operations.

By the same tracer technique the movements of sand in coastal waters and of pebbles on beaches can be determined. Atomic scientists, working in conjunction with the Nature Conservancy, drilled holes in thousands of pebbles and filled them with resin pellets 'labelled' with barium 140 and lanthanum 140; the pebbles were put into the sea on the English coast and their movements traced with portable detectors. Another technique recently developed consists in impregnating the surfaces of the pebbles with silver 110, gold 198, and other isotopes; in a field trial in which the pebbles were put into the sea, 6 per cent of them were recovered after two days and another 3 per cent after three weeks, during which time they had moved up to a mile.

These tracing operations yield valuable information for the study of coastal build-up and erosion. Similarly, the circulation of the atmosphere—especially what the meteorologists call 'north–south mixing'—can be investigated with the help of short-lived isotopes.

Labelling and tracing is finding widespread use in various fields of research. By labelling insects, for instance, it is possible to study how they transmit animal diseases. Tracers are used to follow fertilizers from the soil through the plant; the information obtained helps farmers to decide when and how to apply fertilizing materials to their crops. In Australia, mistletoe—a parasitic shrub when robbed of its sentimental value for Christmas—annually destroys great amounts of eucalyptus trees, an important source of timber in the country's economy. Australian scientists have used cobalt, iron, and zinc isotopes as tracers to study their movements from the eucalyptus tree, the host plant, into the mistletoe, the parasite. By determining the extent of this movement an estimation could be made of the efficacy of various compounds in destroying the mistletoe without harming the trees. Danish scientists mixed the mercury contained in fungicides with mercury isotopes to find out how much of it was actually left on the plants after spraying.

We have already mentioned a number of uses of radioisotopes in medicine. The tracer technique adds a few more in the field of medical research. Cancer and leukæmia are being investigated by this new method; tracers have been used to show that the loss of calcium from the bones continues at a steady rate into old age, but that elderly people have increasing difficulty in absorbing calcium from their food. Tracers may soon provide a means for diagnosing anæmia just as they are now being used to diagnose thyroid disorders. Absorption by the body of vitamin B_{12}, which contains cobalt and seems to be essential for growth, is being studied in connection with anæmia.

American scientists have put fleas on water containing radioactive cerium, and allowed them to resume their normal life.

The idea was to find out how fleas spread plague from animals to Man, and much valuable information has already been gathered from the experiment.

Archæologists with the Geiger Counter

Every now and then we come upon the term carbon 14 in this or that connection. It is, in fact, one of the most important isotopes. This isotope of the basic organic element, carbon, is extremely valuable in medical and biological research. With its help, the biologist is rapidly gaining more and more information about the intricate processes taking place in a living organism. Sugar, fats and other foodstuffs can be fed to animals, labelled with C-14, and therefore traceable all over the organism. It reveals the way in which complex molecules are broken up and used as 'bricks' to build new molecules—proteins, blood, bone. It is just as if the biologist could see his C-14 atom changing from one molecule to another as it completes its journey from food intake to excretion. C-14 has already brought about a major change in our notions of the metabolism of foodstuffs. Previously it was assumed that food was a kind of fuel supplying energy to the body, or repairing wastage and damage in tissues. It seems now that there is a continuous flow of rapid chemical reactions. Protein molecules are taken to pieces and reassembled from the raw material in a kind of 'pool' of molecular fragments within about half an hour of intake. Iron moves in and out of the blood within a matter of minutes. Practically all parts of the organism are continually being rebuilt, including the crystalline structure of the bones. "The miracle of it is," says Sir John Cockcroft, "that our bodies on the whole function so well!"

It is certainly possible that one of these days the answer to the question of the cancerous cell, of the cell growth getting out of control, may come from C-14; that it might even help to find a cure for that greatest of all killer diseases. And there is another huge question mark that has been haunting biochemists for a long time: how does photo-synthesis work— how do the plants turn carbon dioxide, with the aid of light, into sugar, starch and other complex compounds? If we knew the answer we could perhaps produce all our food directly in chemical factories without going the roundabout way of growing it in the fields and orchards and of fattening herds of cattle.

Carbon 14 has been found to be a vital tool in photo-synthesis research. In Britain, America, and Russia work is going on much on the same lines. The plants used in these experiments are allowed to breathe carbon dioxide containing a small proportion of C-14, which is then traced on its way through the organism. Professor Melvin Calvin, of the University of California, described some of his work at the 1955 Geneva Conference. He spoke of a new feature of the photo-synthetic process which had been found: it appears that carbon dioxide from the atmosphere is first absorbed by an organic compound in the plant called phospho-glyceric acid; this chemical is then able to go through a series of transformations resulting in the production of sugar and starch. The phospho-glyceric acid itself is regenerated in the process and starts another chain of transformations.

What if the light is shut off? Within a minute or so of being put in the dark the amount of phospho-glyceric acid, says Professor Calvin, is doubled, while that of other chemicals in the plant's complex chain of processes decreases almost to nil!

The Russians claimed some remarkable results at about the same time. They found that they could produce substantial amounts of protein in plants by varying the conditions of photo-synthesis. Normally, the amounts of protein in plants are very small, though important, as they are necessary for the functioning of certain mechanisms in the plant. In these experiments C-14 played a vital part; and when one day the secrets of photo-synthesis are revealed to us, this great scientific achievement will be due, to a large extent, to the carbon isotope.

However, C-14 is not only manufactured in nuclear reactors, it occurs in Nature. Cosmic-ray bombardment of nitrogen, which makes up four-fifths of our atmosphere, results in turning some of the gas into radio-carbon, which combines with oxygen to form carbon dioxide. All the carbon in animals and plants is derived directly or indirectly from the CO_2 in the atmosphere. Upon the death of an animal or plant the carbon starts to decay, with a half-life of 5500 years—which is an exceedingly long one for an isotope. During the last few years archæologists have begun to use this heaven-sent opportunity of measuring the ages of their specimens by determining their C-14 content; by this method the age of some organic matter, from bones to timber, can be measured with an accuracy of plus or minus fifty years.

One of the most interesting examples of archæological 'carbon-dating' are the excavations at Jericho, described by Dr Kathleen Kenyon at the Royal Institution in 1957. It was found that the town goes back to Neolithic times, when it had a great stone tower (discovered in 1956). At its side there is a whole series of tip-lines representing different building levels; one of the houses—not the oldest—was dated by the C-14 method to about 6800 BC. The extreme age of that settlement has been an archæological sensation of the first magnitude, all the more as the houses of Jericho's earliest Neolithic level are far from primitive. They are built of solid mud-brick and round in shape, with short, narrow staircases leading down from the entrance. Dr Kenyon believes that some houses had more than one room. As these fascinating excavations are going on there is more and more evidence for the theory that the first traces of civilized life go back much farther than has hitherto been believed.

Archæologists have by now become quite used to handling the Geiger counter. In 1956 a fossilized fish was chipped out of a rock near Thurso in the north of Scotland, and found to contain no less than 0·32 per cent of uranium and 0·51 per cent of thorium; the radiation from these elements was sufficient to blacken photographic plates. The fish was sent to the Geological Museum in London, where it was taken to pieces in the hope of finding new facts on the natural atomic transformations which are going on continually in the depths of the earth. The fish was of a primitive species called *homostius*, and must have been swimming about the Scottish sea something like 300 million years ago. It is believed to have been radio-activated not by the local rocks but by thinly distributed amounts of uranium and thorium in the granites along the eastern boundaries of Sutherland, and that the water run off that area was sufficiently radio-active to impregnate the fish 'down-stream', perhaps in some complicated nuclear exchange process. Research workers are convinced that many more 'hot' fish will be found in the region.

Another radio-isotope, potassium 40, has been used to determine the age of some meteorites which fell in northern Kansas in 1948. Scientists found that these pieces of rock may well have been travelling in space for 240–280 million years as part of a planet that had been in existence for another 4200 million years before breaking up, and must have come into existence about the time when our own earth was formed. These findings were based on the measurement of the potassium 40 and argon 40 amounts in the meteorites (the first decays into the second); two other isotopes, tritium (hydrogen 3) and helium 3, provided the evidence of cosmic-ray bombardment in space during the meteorites' journey.

To return to man-initiated radio-activity: we know how elements are 'cooked' in nuclear reactors so that they become unstable isotopes. For research purposes, however, it is necessary to separate groups of isotopes; investigation of the fundamental nuclear properties of separated radio-active isotopes is most important in extending our knowledge of nuclear physics as well as in the designing of reactors for the future. There are, for instance, various types of plutonium which may be generated in a reactor, and their examination cannot be carried out unless they are separated from each other.

This is done by electro-magnetic separators; every nuclear research installation has one. But HERMES (Heavy Element and Radio-active Material Electro-magnetic Separator), designed and built at Harwell, is probably the largest and most efficient of its kind, and certainly the biggest and most complex machine in Western Europe ever built into a sealed space. The hermetically sealed building in which HERMES is enclosed is 21 ft × 25 ft and 14 ft high. As it is dealing with highly active and poisonous material, the machine is remotely controlled from an adjoining room, and maintenance and servicing are carried out by engineers in heavy 'frogman' rubber suits, who enter through a corridor serving as an airlock. The frogman suits are kept under pressure as long as their occupants are in the machine buildings, so that any radio-active dust particles are kept out.

HERMES separates the isotope groups by accelerating a beam of electrically charged atoms through regions where electrical and magnetic forces cause the different groups, with slightly different weight, to follow separate paths through the machine. Its sensitivity is so great that it can separate isotopes of plutonium in milligram range quantities; it may also be used to separate radio-active isotopes from non-active elements.

Britain's New Industry

Among the quiet and lovely Chiltern Hills of Buckinghamshire, 25 miles from London, lies Amersham, a small market town which seems to have little connection with this modern age. But to a world-wide company of scientists, engineers, and doctors, Amersham means the very essence of the peaceful application of atomic energy, for here is the great Radio-chemical Centre which provides some fifty different countries —including a number behind the Iron Curtain—annually with 20,000–25,000 consignments of radio-isotopes worth £500,000.

Amersham is the only centre of its kind in the world, dealing as it does with natural as well as artificial radio-active material. The comparable American radio-chemical institution at Oak Ridge does not work on the same scale; in fact, the USA itself is Amersham's customer (the biggest one for carbon 14, to mention only one item from the sales list).

There is an Isotope Division at Harwell for the direct sale of materials, but Amersham, which is affiliated to Harwell under the Atomic Energy Authority, deals with all those which need chemical processing before they can be used in industry, research, or medicine. One of the by-products of atomic energy has been the rapid fusion of the scientific branches of physics and chemistry, which used to be kept so religiously apart in the schools and universities. Today they overlap to an increasing extent in nuclear science, but in Amersham the emphasis lies on the chemical side. Until the early 1950s the work was done more or less on the conventional lines of a chemical factory, although under more stringent safety conditions. From 1954 onwards new laboratories incorporating a variety of ingenious and unconventional devices were brought into operation, with the result that the scale of production has gone up three or four times and products have been improved substantially. For example, the best carbon 14 made recently has shown nearly 50 per cent 'isotopic abundance', as the radio-chemists call it, compared with less than 2 per cent a few years ago!

The visitor who enters the Amersham establishment has to conform with the strict safety regulations which are rigidly enforced in all buildings where radio-active material is being handled. The cloakrooms where the staff change in and out of their overalls and plastic shoe-covers are equipped with hand monitors for alpha, beta, and gamma radiation; they are large steel cabinets into which one puts one's hands, and the built-in Geiger counters click away registering the amount of radio-activity that one has accumulated at work. Every staff member must wear on his or her lapel a 'body film', a little metal frame with a film in it which is developed to see if there is excessive radio-activity, and twice-a-month breath tests are carried out to check the breath for radon gas. In the washroom the taps are foot-operated, and even the paper towels are not just thrown into the dustbin—they are collected and taken to Harwell to be burnt with other potentially radio-active waste.

In the laboratories something of the worlds of H. G. Wells and Orwell comes to life in the shape of atom age equipment. The 'hot boxes', in which radio-active material is handled, have very thick lead walls and glass, perspex, or quartz windows to shield the workers; the less dangerous materials require only 'glove boxes', cabinets with two rubber gloves fitted in holes in the window so that the worker can use his own hands, but the highly active isotopes are manipulated by the 'master-slave' mechanism—outside the box the worker carries out a series of hand-and-finger movements which are faithfully reproduced by a pair of mechanical hands inside, behind 3-ft thick windows. The accuracy with which test-tubes can be picked up, liquids poured into bottles, caps turned, and the tiniest parts handled must be seen to be believed.

Some of the hot boxes have built-in vacuum cleaners to extricate the dust. Women with Geiger counters on gliders, which look like mine detectors, go over every inch of the polished floor. Switchboards with knobs and dials are to be found at almost every corner. A man in an over-size, transparent plastic suit fixed to the end of a movable transparent tunnel is carrying out maintenance work in one of the three cave-like lead chambers where radio-cæsium is produced. He speaks into his 'walkie-talkie' radio-telephone set as he works in his 'captive man' suit, as the outfit is called. An engineer, with another 'walkie-talkie', directs operations from a distance.

"This little glass tube is worth six thousand pounds," a chemist informs the visitor, pointing to a minute glass container just being filled with some innocent-looking powder. "But it'll last for more than five thousand years. It's carbon 14."

"Why is it so expensive?"

"Because it takes a year or two to make it. A compound containing nitrogen is put into the reactor, and as time goes on a good deal of the nitrogen is transmuted into radio-carbon by capturing neutrons. Here at Amersham we separate the carbon from the nitrogen compound—and there you have the end product."

Iodine 131, the visitor learns, is much cheaper; the tellurium 130 from which it is made needs only a fortnight's irradiation, but it loses half of its mass within a week. Most radio-isotopes are the products of such a transmutation of elements which would have told mediæval alchemists that their dream of a 'philosopher's stone' was not so fantastic after all. Phosphorus 32 is made from sulphur, but sulphur 35 from chlorine 35 . . . and so on.

Isotopes in Aircraft Wings

The rapid decrease in radiating power of many isotopes sets some very difficult problems for the administrative staff. Orders come in from all over the world by letter or cable, and each of the 700 items in the Centre's catalogue requires individual handling when dispatched. At the packing department, radiation monitors indicate the maximum radiation levels tolerated by the postal and air authorities. Special vans take the little packets to London airport to get them to their destination as quickly as possible—that is, with a minimum of radiation loss. Many British and some foreign airliners have small compartments in their wingtips where isotope consignments can be carried so that no shielding of passengers, crew, and freight is necessary. The delivery time to Japan or Australia is only four days from London; even in these far-distant places the customer can reckon with getting his delivery within less than seven days from cabling his order to Amersham. In Europe, deliveries are generally carried out within 48 hrs. There must be no idle time between the preparation of the order and its despatch by air, for these materials are far too dangerous and far too precious to keep them lying about.

Radio-isotopes is a new industry in which demand will surpass supply for a long time to come. Amersham plans to increase its production eventually a hundred times over the pre-1954 level, but requirements in all countries are expected to increase even more. In spite of the great variety of artificially produced isotopes, the demand for natural radio-active elements has by no means declined. From 1954 to 1958 Amersham has manufactured about 8000 clinical radium needles and

120,000 radon 'seeds', mainly for British hospitals. The production lines for filling radium containers for medicine and industry have been rebuilt for complete remote-handling while the material is entirely enclosed: a most difficult enterprise with such fine work.

Safety at Amersham is of such a high standard that despite the special danger of its work, the Centre compares very favourably with other industries; even its drainage system has been carefully designed so that no radio-activity goes where it should not. But what about the innumerable recipients of isotopes? Are they aware of the hazards, and do they know how to counter them?

It cannot be expected that everybody using radio-isotopes should be expert enough to know the best way of getting rid of radio-active waste, and a good deal of guesswork is still going on. However, the Radiochemical Centre and similar establishments in Britain, America, and many other countries now using atomic energy will advise the inquirer. Solid wastes can be disposed of by incineration, closed storage, open burial, or drainage out to sea. Incineration is especially valuable for treating animal carcases and as a means to reduce the volume of the solid waste, but it gives rise to active gases and ash. The discharge of the gases should be clear of windows. Burial may be used on permanently enclosed sites at levels depending on the rainfall so that the local groundwater is not contaminated. Even highly radio-active solid wastes can be disposed of safely in the sea provided that all relevant factors are kept in mind: movement of the surface water, the breeding and migratory habits of fish, and the possible hazard to seaweed where it is harvested for food, fertilization, or industrial use. Disposals must be made at points where they cannot contaminate the trawling gear of fishermen.

Isotopes have already become part and parcel of our daily lives; we do not have to go to hospital to become users of their radiation—the packet of sugar we empty into the bowl, the toothpaste tube on the bathroom shelf may have been checked for filling level by radio-isotopes, and we can set our watches by the most accurate clock in the world, regulated by radio-cæsium vibrations. Within a few years isotopes will turn up in many more expected or unexpected places—perhaps the slogan, 'Gamma Washes Whiter', will become quite familiar to us when our ultrasonic washing-machines are equipped with some gamma source to sterilize shirts and socks and napkins.

Yet it was only in 1913 that the word radio-isotope was first used by Dr Frederick Soddy. Before he coined it, radio-chemistry was usually called 'the chemistry of phantoms'. Rarely have scientific phantoms taken on such tangible form within such short time.

VI

NUCLEAR TRANSPORT

'THE ENERGY contained in the atoms of a piece of uranium the size of a golfball could drive an ocean liner through the sea for an indefinite time,' wrote the US Army newspaper, *Stars and Stripes*, in August, 1945, explaining atomic energy to the American soldiers. Ever since the first speculations on the peaceful uses of nuclear power followed in the wake of the Hiroshima and Nagasaki bombs, sea transport has been foremost in everybody's minds. The reason is obvious; there is an invaluable advantage if the fuel does not require replenishment (though the notion of the golfball-size piece of uranium seems to us now a little too optimistic), and there is the constructional possibility of incorporating the necessary heavy shielding in the design.

The first nuclear-powered ship, however, was not meant to serve a peaceful purpose. It was the US submarine *Nautilus*, which began its sea trials in 1955, and which steamed no less than 60,000 miles on a single charge of fuel; during this time the total amount of fuel consumed weighed about 8 lb. The ship would have needed 10,000 tons of oil if it had been propelled by conventional engines. A second submarine, the *Seawolf*, was first equipped with a sodium-cooled reactor. This, however, failed, and a pressurized-water system as in the *Nautilus* was fitted instead. Subsequently, a dozen more craft of the same type, though of varying sizes, were commissioned, the largest being the *Triton*, of 5450 tons, running on two reactors.

In 1956 construction work began on two US warships with nuclear propulsion, a guided-missile cruiser of 14,000 tons, powered by two reactors, to be completed in 1960; and a giant aircraft carrier of 85,000 tons with eight reactors.

The *Nautilus* proved that marine propulsion by atomic energy is technically feasible, but it also proved that despite its very low fuel consumption this form of propulsion is by no means cheap. The cost of power from the *Nautilus* reactor is about six times higher than that of oil-fired commercial ship propulsion. Its fuel is uranium 235, which heats ordinary water; this circulates through a heat exchanger where steam is raised; the temperature and pressure are comparatively low, mainly for safety reasons, and the efficiency rate of converting the heat into power in the steam turbines is no more than 25 per cent.

Russia's Nuclear Icebreaker

If the Russians are building nuclear-powered submarines they are not publicizing this fact. But they have been engaged in another venture, which appears most interesting from various angles: the construction of an atomic icebreaker, the *Lenin*, launched in 1958. She has a cargo capacity of 16,000 tons and a speed of 18 knots, with a power plant of 200,000 kw, 42,000 shp, and four screws. Apart from the extraordinary power provided by the screw propellers, the ship will be equipped with high-pressure waterjets for cutting a passage into the ice; she will also carry helicopters for reconnaissance. The advantage of nuclear power for an icebreaker is the fact that the ship is entirely independent of fuel supplies for very long periods. If necessary, fresh fuel could be brought up by air. This enables the *Lenin* to work differently from conventional icebreakers. She is said to be powerful enough to cut through 6 ft of ice.

America's first nuclear merchant ship, which is expected to be completed in 1960, will be the ns *Savannah* ('ns' standing for 'nuclear ship'). It is being named after the first steamship to cross the Atlantic from Georgia to Liverpool in 1819. The new vessel will be a cargo ship of 10,000 tons with accommodation for sixty passengers, and may be sailing the oceans for about two years before her reactor has to be recharged.

Like the US, Britain is working on nuclear propulsion for submarines. At Dounreay, the land-based prototype of the reactor for the *Dreadnought*, Britain's first atomic submarine, will be built and put into a hull structure representing the actual ship; here the machinery will be tested and the men who will operate it will be trained. The *Dreadnought*'s reactor has been designed on the same lines as that of America's *Nautilus*, with a pressurized-water system. Like the *Nautilus*, the *Dreadnought* is not an economical proposition; but then military constructions never are.

A complete re-orientation in shipbuilding is necessary to

make nuclear marine propulsion really economical. Ships have been designed on the same traditional lines for ages; even the change from the sailing-ship to the steam-driven vessel

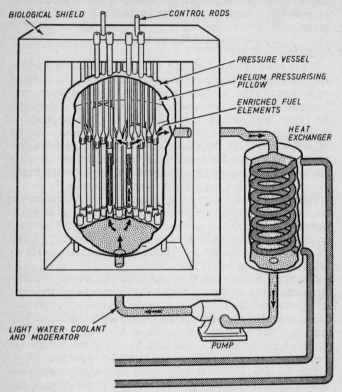

FIG. 9 The pressurized-water reactor—operating with ordinary water under pressure for moderating and cooling the enriched-fuel core—used in the first nuclear submarines and in the *Savannah*.

has not resulted in basic alterations—to put it crudely, the masts were replaced by the funnels. Later, the most daring revolution was that of putting the machines in the stern so that the passengers would have the forward part of the ship to themselves—a change that is still being resisted by many designers. Other minor revolutions were brought about by the special requirements of oil tankers.

Now, however, we seem to have reached a point where the ship-builders will be forced to do some rethinking. Nuclear propulsion for ships is not only a possibility; it will, by the sheer force of its advantages, become the normal form of marine propulsion within the next quarter of a century, at least for larger craft.

Perhaps the most promising new idea is that of separating the power unit from the passenger or cargo vessel—returning, as it were, to the engine-and-coach form of traditional rail transport. Powerful nuclear tugs could be constructed; they could be in continuous operation at sea, towing liners or freighters from port to port. There would be no fuel-wasting waits while the ship herself is being loaded or unloaded; the tug would return to sea straight away with another vessel in tow, and of course with another machine crew. It would require refuelling only every six or nine months.

Such a tug could be built very large and fitted with buoyancy tanks that would make it practically unsinkable. The passenger or freight unit, on the other hand, could be designed without any regard to such requirements as material strength to contain the heavy conventional machinery; there will be no propulsion machines in the towed unit. It might, therefore, prove to be much more practical—and a great deal cheaper—to build it from prefabricated plastic parts; we might even return, after many decades of iron and steel-built vessels, to the wooden ship. It can now be designed completely streamlined, without funnels, perhaps totally enclosed and air-conditioned.

Although the capital investment in a great number of nuclear tugs would be infinitely smaller than it is now, with an expensive propulsion unit in every ship, some companies might prefer to build very large and fast nuclear-powered liners, and these might be designed after the so-called hydro-foil system, which has created a good deal of interest lately. These ships have underwater 'wings' fixed to the hull; at a certain speed the body of the vessel begins to rise from the water, leaving only the wings and screws in it. Some hydrofoil boats of small size are already in existence: as pleasure craft and as ferry-boats on lakes where oil-drilling is proceeding from floating platforms.

But we do not have to look to the future for revolutionary

designs in shipbuilding. One of the most imaginative ideas is already being carried out.

The Nuclear-powered Submarine Tanker

At least four very large oil tankers, built as submarines and nuclear-powered, are at present on the drawing-boards. A

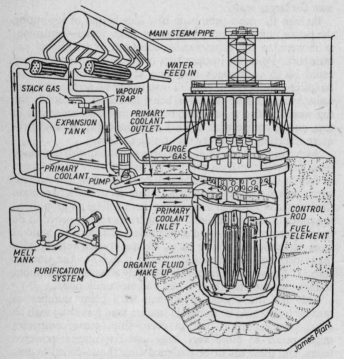

FIG. 10   Reactor assembly of a nuclear oil tanker.

combination of British and Swiss companies is building three 68,000-ton ships of this type, and two big British firms, the Mitchell Engineering Group and Saunders-Roe, are going ahead with the construction of the largest vessel ever built, a nuclear-powered submarine tanker of 100,000 tons.

Only once since submarines have been in existence has this

type of ship been used for commercial purposes. During the First World War, Germany built a big U-boat for breaking the Allied blockade by bringing from America—at that time still neutral—some scarce raw materials needed by the German war economy. For the following thirty-five years, however, no attention was paid to the possibilities of using submarines for anything but military purposes where secrecy and stealth are of supreme importance.

In the middle 1950s, Sir George Thomson, the British Nobel Prize winner, Sir J. J. Thomson's son and himself an outstanding nuclear physicist, suggested the possibility of building large submarine liners and cargo ships, which would be much more efficient hydrodynamically than surface vessels. Hitherto, he said, such ships could not be considered because the conventional fuels demand an ample supply of oxygen. Nuclear plant does not need much oxygen. Sir George foresaw submarine liners travelling at over twice the speed of the present surface ships, and at less cost; the economic advantage would be particularly great in the transport of bulk materials.

Sir George's idea, which was taken up by a number of progressive designers and engineers, may turn out to be the point of departure for the greatest revolution in marine transport since 'Fulton's Folly' steamed up the Hudson a century and a half ago. If the first commercial submarines are successful it may mean the beginning of an era of universal underwater travel and transport. In fact, it would be a development just as logical as the tendency in air travel to take the airliners high above the turbulent weather in the lower regions of the atmosphere. The same principle can be applied at sea, where the upper regions of the water are continuously disturbed by waves and currents; in addition, a surface ship, travelling as it does in two elements, is also affected by the wind.

The submarine moves in a far quieter sphere. It is secure from storms, waves and surface drag, and can make its way with a minimum of resistance. For this reason, speeds up to 60 knots—more than double that of the *Queen Mary*—could well be achieved, with a resulting reduction of operational costs. An extensive hydrodynamic research programme was started in the Saunders-Roe laboratories in the Isle of Wight in 1957. Eight models were tested in a towing tank to determine the most practical body shape. As a number of oil companies were showing great interest in the project, it was decided to design the 100,000-ton submarine as a tanker.

The United Kingdom AEA has meanwhile been going ahead with its studies of reactor and shielding problems for submarine and surface-ship propulsion. LIDO, at Harwell, has been specializing, among other things, in submarine research. A reactor core of enriched uranium plate-type fuel elements, about the size of a tea-chest, is suspended from a trolley running on rails over a water-basin. In the wall of the basin aluminium windows have been set to permit shielding experiments. Obviously, the problem of safety from reactor radiation is one of the most important to be solved before a nuclear submarine tanker can put to sea. Other factors on which Harwell scientists have been working for many years concern the types of nuclear power plant best suited for various marine applications, the kind of fuel required, as well as capital and operating costs. A team of specialists from the British Shipbuilding Research Association is working with the nuclear engineers.

It may well turn out, [said the 1957 report of the AEA] that the problem of marine propulsion divides itself into two separate fields. The large ship which spends most of its time at sea, such as a tanker, might be powered by a scaled-down version of the Calder Hall type of reactor; this would involve comparatively little development effort and offers the greatest chance of being competitive in the near future. For smaller ships it will probably be necessary to develop a new type of reactor and two systems are being studied with this object. The first is an organic-liquid-moderated reactor which might be built in small sizes to give outputs of the order of 20,000 shaft horsepower or less. It has the advantage over the water-moderated reactor of having a lower system pressure and few if any corrosion problems. Like the pressurized-water reactor, however, it calls for enriched fuel. On the other hand the organic liquid becomes less radio-active when irradiated than water, and so the shielding of the external heat exchanger circuit can be reduced or even eliminated.

A heavy-water, gas-cooled reactor is the second possibility for ship propulsion. It would have the advantage of using a fuel of lower enrichment than the organic-liquid reactor, and the technology of fuel elements and heat removal would be similar to that already developed for large power reactors.

The organic liquid which would be suitable as a moderator

144

in smaller ship's reactors may be diphenyl, terphenyl, or similar liquids. They form polymers, large or compound molecules, under irradiation, but not at too high a rate to make the system uneconomic. The great advantage of the organic moderator in ship propulsion is the high temperature which can be reached with it, while the pressure can be much lower than in the pressurized-water system as used, for instance, in the American *Nautilus*.

What about the fuel? Natural uranium would be the cheapest, though not the most economical. But as soon as enough plutonium has been produced by land-based reactors this might prove to be the ideal fuel for ships, and should in the long run become competitive with oil. Fast reactors have the additional convenience of being very compact, which would be important in designing power units for commercial craft. NEPTUNE, the Harwell research reactor for naval submarine propulsion, whose programme is co-ordinated with that of Dounreay, uses enriched uranium as fuel and ordinary water in a non-pressurized system as moderator. It has no cooling system, as only a few watts of heat are generated. NEPTUNE is not meant to supply data for commercial ship's units.

Two newly-formed industrial groups in Britain have been working independently on nuclear-powered surface-tanker projects since 1956; one is the Hawker Siddeley–John Brown Nuclear Construction Company (John Brown are the builders of the *Queen Mary* and the *Queen Elizabeth*), the other combination is that of the engineering firm of Babcock and Wilcox with Cammell Laird, the shipbuilders. The first group intends to construct a tanker of 80,000 tons capacity (*ie* nearly as big as the *Queen Mary*) at a cost of £10–12 million, which may be ready for launching in 1963; an Admiralty-sponsored committee is helping with advice. The other project concerns a 65,000-ton tanker. Both projects are to be fully commercial— that is, they will have to pay their own way and compete in the international shipping market.

After their *Savannah*, the Americans will build another passenger and freight ship with a deadweight cargo capacity of 12,000 tons. The cost of construction has been estimated at $42 million; the ship, in contrast to the British tankers, is not intended to be economic. It will be using a *Nautilus*-type reactor, which is particularly expensive in operation.

It is to be hoped that the designers and constructors of nuclear-powered ships will be aware of the special dangers in case of a collision or crash. If such a vessel happened to collide, say, with one of the piers of Tower Bridge, the entire Pool of London might become radio-active. This is an engineering problem that must be solved before the first commercial atom-powered ship puts to sea.

One of the somewhat paradoxical effects of the introduction of nuclear power into shipping is that the machinery will have to return to the middle of the ship. Owing to the great weight of the nuclear-power unit, it cannot be placed astern. Thus the only major innovation in shipbuilding in the last few decades will be undone.

The Atomic Aeroplane

Next to the sea, the air seems to attract the interest of nuclear-propulsion engineers. We have heard and read a good deal of tests, experiments, and research work in this field in various countries, and any day an atom powered aircraft may start on its first flight.

Even if it does become airborne and land without a hitch, this does not necessarily mean that nuclear flight is just around the corner; for there is one formidable problem which must be solved before we can expect the new form of propulsion to supersede the present ones. It is the problem of reliability.

Calder Hall, the world's first nuclear-power station, has proved extremely reliable in operation. However, it has two reactors; as a rule, both are running, but if for some reason or other one of them stops or has to be shut down, the other one continues to produce electricity. Should both reactors stop, the customers of the national electricity grid would not even notice it because there are plenty more power stations supplying electric current. Even if a nuclear-power station serving some isolated area would have to shut down, it would not be a matter of life and death to the population (hospitals usually have their own emergency power supply). This is not merely a hypothetical case; there may be a number of reasons why a reactor has to shut down occasionally—in ten or twenty years we may be so advanced in reactor design that this possibility can be disregarded; due to the radio-activity of the plant, maintenance is still more complicated than with conventional machines or engines, and therefore the reactor may be out of action for several hours or days.

But what would happen if the reactor of an aircraft stopped suddenly in mid-air? Here the problem of reliability is crucial; it is literally a matter of life and death to the passengers and crew: the 'plane would crash if its power failed. Ships will perhaps be equipped with at least two reactors, so that if one fails the other can still produce enough power for travel at reduced speed. Two reactors in an aircraft, however, would be forbiddingly heavy and make the 'plane uneconomical in operation.

For this reason many experts believe that we are still a rather long way from an economical civil aircraft powered by atomic energy. But there are also other problems. An aeroplane must be able to reduce its power output quickly and substantially for landing. The activity of a slow-neutron reactor cannot be reduced drastically because of the danger that amounts of xenon gas may be built up. The xenon danger can be avoided by using fast neutron fission, but this would severely limit the rate at which heat can be extracted from a given quantity of fuel. In practical terms this would mean that each kilogram of fuel would not yield more than a few thousand kilowatts of heat, and that the fuel will have to be replenished rather frequently—and this will affect the economy of operation.

Highly enriched uranium 235 would be the most suitable fuel for aircraft reactors; it requires a much smaller plant, and it avoids the xenon gas risk. It is, however, rather expensive. A mixture of highly enriched U-235 and natural uranium may be used for reasons of cost, but this would mean a larger reactor system. Even more than in the case of marine propulsion, nuclear energy in the air will become really economical only when large and therefore cheaper quantities of the highly concentrated fuel plutonium become available from our land-based reactors.

The weight of an airborne reactor is, of course, the great headache for the construction engineers. The most optimistic calculation speaks of 1 kw output per cubic centimetre of core, or 30,000 kw of heat per cubic foot. This is not too bad, but there is the problem of the shielding, which assumes major proportions if applied to a confined space such as that of an aircraft. The shield around a reactor must fulfil three functions; it must slow down any fast neutrons escaping from the core, it must absorb slow neutrons, and it must absorb gamma rays from the core. Lead, steel, and concrete are suitable materials for these purposes; a lead or steel shield has to be 2 ft thick, a concrete one 7 ft.

The weight of such shields would be formidable, and to make an aeroplane with a heavy reactor and a heavy shield fly is certainly a difficult task. It has been suggested that rocket motors would be necessary to get a nuclear 'plane off the ground, but this might outweigh any advantages to be gained from nuclear propulsion. An alternative idea is that of shielding not the reactor but the people in the aircraft; this would be feasible only in a military 'plane with a comparatively small number of people on board. Even the comparatively light 'hydrogen-metal' shield—a multi-layer sandwich of steel and water—would not be light enough to solve the problem.

Flying Test-beds

In the face of these huge question marks, the discussion on the most practical and economic way of transforming the heat from the reactor into propelling energy seems to be of secondary importance. There is, however, general agreement that some form of turbojet propulsion will be used, with 'conventional' jets at the business end of the turbine. Heat transfer from the reactor could be achieved by either gas or a liquid coolant such as molten sodium metal; caustic soda and fused fluorides have also been considered. The question is which coolant would be most effective while requiring the least quantity of shielding. It has even been suggested that a nuclear aircraft might be driven by a steam turbine so that ordinary water can be used.

The most likely design to be adopted, however, is one in which the reactor heat produces a flow of gas at high pressure in the heat exchanger; this will go into the gas turbine and then be discharged backwards in a jet. If the jets are not to be unsuitably large, temperatures of at least 1500° F will be required.

All these facts and factors seem to indicate that, at least for the immediate future, any development of nuclear aircraft must be restricted to the military field where economic considerations do not play a major part. Indeed, it has been said that the only application of nuclear propulsion in the air would be the supersonic low-level bomber. Britain, America, and Russia are all doing research work in this field. In Britain, Rolls-Royce, the Hawker-Siddeley group, Bristol Aeroplanes, Fairey Aviation, and de Havilland have been engaged in it for some time, and Saunders-Roe may use their 'mothballed' three Princess flying-boats as flying test-beds—that is, reactors would be put on board to study a number of problems in the air. Rolls-Royce hope to develop light-weight nuclear reactors with liquid-metal coolants; lithium, bismuth, mercury, and lead have been investigated from this angle.

In America, the US Air Force and the Convair Aircraft Company have been flying B-36 bombers carrying atomic reactors over Texas and New Mexico since early in 1956. The reactors were never operated during takeoffs and landings, but only when cruising over little-populated areas. The object was the study of weight distribution and, of course, shielding. At the Oak Ridge National Laboratory an arrangement of four steel towers with a reactor suspended between them has been used for similar purposes.

The aircraft engineers seem to be well aware of the public concern which would arise if regular test flights with 'hot' reactors were made over populated areas, adding yet another hazard to modern life. What, indeed, would be the risk to earthbound citizens if an atom-powered aircraft crashed? Some experts say that an area of 100 square miles would be affected by scattered radio-activity. A ceramic form of fuel would limit the danger considerably, while liquid fuel, or one that melts at low temperatures or is easily inflammable, would mean a considerable risk. The danger that a reactor might blow up in the air like an atom bomb, however, is negligible.

The Russians, too, are using four-engined bombers as flying test-beds for reactors, and their research work seems to be similarly directed towards the development of military nuclear-powered aircraft. To them the advantages of inter-continental 'carrier planes' for missile-launching and aerial inspection, of machines which can fly from three months to a year without refuelling, must seem very tempting. They are also known to be working on nuclear-propulsion units for guided missiles and sputnik-launching rockets, and of course for interplanetary spaceships (see Chapter VII).

The Soviet authorities announced in December, 1957, that Professor Tupolev, their leading aircraft designer and creator of the famous jet airliner Tu-104, was in charge of these development schemes. Tupolev's design, too, is based on the turbojet principle: tubes are carrying hot air or liquid from the reactor—at temperatures between 1650 and 1850° F—to the heat exchangers where it is turned into gas for the turbines. 'There are, however, paramount difficulties still to be over-come,' wrote a military expert in the Soviet popular science magazine, *Young Technician*, in November, 1957, 'there are no materials which could stand the enormous heat, no effective coolants, and no lightweight materials which could effectively absorb nuclear radiation.' In the light of this admission it sounds rather optimistic when he says that 'the time is not far off when the first atomic aircraft will leave the ground'. References to 'the first test flights of an atomic aviation power plant', which had already taken place, seemed therefore to refer to flying test-beds only. Calculations of nuclear fuel consumption as compared with that of conventional aircraft come to about the same in Russia as in the West: a 2-jet Tu-104, say the Russians, requires 150 tons of fuel for a journey from Moscow to Vladivostok; a nuclear-powered 'plane would not consume more than $2\frac{1}{2}$–3 oz of uranium for the same trip. The Society of British Aircraft Constructors—which believes that large bombers and ocean-patrol flying-boats will be the first nuclear-powered aircraft—estimates that a long-range conventional 'plane would need 100,000 lb of fuel for a distance of 5500 miles and that an atom-powered one could do the journey on 0·05 lb of U-235.

Atomic Air Tugs?

The Russians, who do not seem to be worried about the commercial side of their projects, are also working on non-military atomic aircraft. Their favourite scheme in that field is a weird-looking craft called 'convertiplane': a large airliner with three helicopter rotors, one on each wingtip and a third on the tail, which is bent upward. These rotors are to be nuclear-powered, probably by three separate reactors. The craft would fly like an ordinary helicopter, the forward move-ment being achieved by adjusting the pitch of the rotor blades. 'It could take an expedition from Moscow to the Antarctic in a day,' says the Soviet Defence Ministry which published the design, 'and it does not need airfields to take off or land.'

Still, if the 'convertiplane' is to carry passengers, all the formidable problems which we have discussed would first have to be solved. But there is a British idea which is still more radical, and may provide the answer to a good many questions. It is the idea of the atomic aerial 'tug'.

This is, in fact, the adaptation of the atomic marine tug scheme for air transport, and most of the advantages would be the same. There are two versions of the idea. One suggests the construction of very fast atom-powered tractor units which would stay aloft over the sea, cruising from continent to continent without ever landing except for occasional maintenance, refuelling, and repairs. Land-based non-atomic airliners would fly up from the airports under their own power, hook up, and be pulled to points near their destinations through the stratosphere at supersonic speed. There they unhitch and proceed down for the landing while the tug hooks up with another airliner for the return journey—and so on. The airliners would not have to carry more fuel than they need for the two trips to and from the tug, while the tug itself can carry on high above the weather at almost constant cruising speed. It would have two crews on board to work in shifts, and relief crews would be carried up after a certain number of days.

The other version of this idea suggests nuclear-powered, windowless, delta-shaped transport 'planes travelling at speeds up to 2000 mph between, say, Europe and America, carrying at least 100 passengers and making ten crossings a day, flying at great height. Passengers and freight will be flown up to them in tenders from airports near the turning points, but the tenders will hitch up with them only until the passengers have been transferred to the main craft through a pressurized passage-way, and then return to the airport.

The Atlantic crossing would not take more than a couple of hours, and the passengers would lose little by not being able to look out of the windows—at a height of 10 or 12 miles there is nothing to see. It would be difficult to build windows in such an aircraft because of the great difference in atmospheric pressure inside and outside. The passengers will get a meal and perhaps a film show, and they can move freely about the spacious 'plane.

The crew could be limited to three or four, apart from the stewards, because the machinery operates completely automatically. Fares could be kept low because of the great economy of the system; a single machine could transport 1000 people across the Atlantic per day, half as many as the largest ocean liners. The tenders could be kept small, carrying about twenty-five passengers each, and the main craft would pick them up over three to five airports on each side of the Atlantic to use all available space.

Some system of this kind may come into operation as soon as the main problems of nuclear reactors for air transport have been solved. It would at any rate solve those connected with the tricky business of starting and landing. These tugs or continuous-transport 'planes would never take off or come down with passengers when they are due for their routine overhaul and refuelling, and they would be allotted special airfields far from densely populated areas, where there is little air traffic, and facilities are provided for their specific requirements. Once up in their orbits, they are safe from interference by other aircraft; their altitude would be determined by international agreement. But they might perhaps occasionally meet some unmanned, nuclear-powered craft also circling above the seas and continents for months on end—airborne television relay stations, which could make world-wide reception possible.

The Prospects for Nuclear Motor-cars

In the bleak post-war winter of 1945–46 the people of London had a good laugh. A seventy-one-year-old doctor invited the Minister of Fuel and Power to a trip in his invention, the 'first atomic car'. The Minister, an open-minded man, thought it his duty to investigate the matter and try the thing out himself, even at the risk of stepping into eternity by stepping into the car. He kept the appointment. The inventor, however, did not; later he explained that 'people with sinister motives' had stolen the car. A few months later the inventor's name appeared again in the papers; he had been sent to prison for obtaining money under false pretences.

The story is significant for the unlimited confidence in nuclear energy during those early years of the atomic age. Today no Minister who knows anything about the subject would bother even to read a letter from an inventor claiming to have built a nuclear-powered car. The problems and difficulties are so well known that the mere term 'inventing' sounds absurd in this connection.

First, the cost. An atomic reactor even of the smallest

possible size—which is determined by 'criticality', as we know —costs hundreds of thousands of pounds. Secondly, the weight and bulk of the shielding necessary to prevent the driver from being irradiated to death. It would have to be a very large car indeed, much larger than the police would ever permit to roam the countryside, let alone our cities. "I see no hope for the nuclear motor-car," said Sir George Thomson in his capacity as the President of the Physical Section of the British Association in 1956. He expressed not only his own opinion but also that of the overwhelming majority of motor-car engineers and research workers.

It cannot be denied, though, that there have been a few voices in the wilderness expressing confidence in the nuclear car. Mr Benson Ford, Henry Ford's grandson, predicted in 1955 that "atomic or solar energy may replace the petrol-engine". He did not, however, go into technical details or announce that the Ford Company had embarked on the construction of a prototype.

At about the same time a Soviet source claimed that Russian scientists had 'developed a nuclear-powered car operating for weeks on a few grams of uranium'. Professor Romadin was mentioned as the designer. A few data were also given: lead was used as a coolant, carrying the reactor heat to the heat exchanger. As to the most important item of shielding, all that was said was that 'a new metal alloy' was used. There were no details about the weight, size, cost, performance, or safety of the car, and nothing more has been heard of it since.

Even if such a road vehicle could be built, would it be a good idea? A century and a half ago, when the first steam-engines came into use, some inventors such as the very gifted Richard Trevithick built steam-powered road vehicles. The technical difficulties were not insuperable, but was it a good idea—that is, did the peculiar properties of the steam-engine suit the peculiar requirements of the road? Although there was no other form of mechanical propulsion until late in the 19th century, the steam-car was abandoned because it was not a suitable means of transport. As soon as the steam-engine was put on rails and made to run on its own special permanent way it was an entirely different matter.

Today, and tomorrow, we have the petrol engine, the diesel engine, and the gas turbine (now in the course of development for this purpose) as the most suitable and economical prime movers for road vehicles. We do not need to rack our brains how to adapt nuclear energy to motor-cars. We shall be saving so much oil by switching to nuclear energy in other spheres of power production that there will be enough of it for quite a while.

What about nuclear locomotives? Here the difficulties are not as forbidding as with the motor-car. Several American companies have been authorized by the Atomic Energy Commission to study the problem. Professor Dr Lyle B. Borst of the University of Utah, who had helped with the construction of AEC reactors at Brookhaven and worked at Oak Ridge and Hanford during the war, published in 1954 the design of a possible nuclear-powered railway engine. It would be 160 ft long, with thirty wheels; the reactor, running on liquid-uranium fuel, would be 2 by 3 by 3 ft and the steel shielding, weighing 200 tons, would be 4 in. thick. Operating for one year on 11 lb of uranium the engine would develop 7000 hp, or four times the power of a comparable diesel-electric locomotive (the cost, $1·2 million, would be only twice as much). The reactor heat would be transferred to steam turbines coupled to electric generators.

There is no doubt that such an engine could be built and work satisfactorily. But would it be worth while? Is not the present trend in most countries—to electrify as much as feasible of the rail network (while running diesel-electric locomotives on non-electrified lines)—a much more practical system of utilizing atomic energy, by way of the nuclear-power stations, for rail transport? There is also the danger that a railway accident might spread radio-activity over a wide area. Fascinating as the possibilities of nuclear energy are in numerous fields there would be no point in imposing it on forms of transport which are providing perfectly satisfactory service with the means now at their disposal. As soon as they cease to do so, as soon as technically or economically a change would bring real advantages our designers and engineers will be the first to suggest it.

VII

AS FAR AS THOUGHT CAN REACH

THERE IS no doubt that—provided Man can overcome his suicidal tendencies—atomic energy is bound to bring about the greatest change which any invention or discovery has ever caused on Earth, next to the theft of the heavenly fire by Prometheus for the benefit of mankind. If all goes well, the first hundred years of atomic energy will end with an abundance of power everywhere, with the rapidly increasing development of the regions and nations so far neglected by civilization, and with everybody reaping the full benefit of the miraculous forces of radio-activity.

This is the prospect before us and our children even if only the fission process is utilized. But there is more to come. Thermo-nuclear power, the fusion process, the tamed energy of the hydrogen bomb will be at our disposal in a few years.

Atomic energy, as we know, is freed when the nuclei of a heavy atom such as uranium or the artificial element plutonium are split. It can also be produced when the nuclei of the lightest elements combine to form heavier ones. In the H-bomb this happens in an uncontrolled chain reaction. Since 1948, British scientists—among them Sir George Thomson—at Cambridge, London, Harwell, and Aldermaston have been working on the problem of taming the power of nuclear fusion for peaceful purposes; American scientists have done this since 1952 at Princeton, Oak Ridge, Los Alamos, and Livermore; Russian scientists since 1950 at Moscow; Swedish scientists since 1956 at Stockholm and Uppsala. France has its special laboratory for fusion research at Fontenay, and German laboratories and universities—at Göttingen, Hamburg, Kiel, and Aachen—are engaged in similar work.

The theory of nuclear fusion was discovered by Cockcroft and Walton during the 'golden age' of nuclear research, now irreverently called the Stone Age (to be precise: in 1932–33), at the Cavendish Laboratory, Cambridge, and followed up by Professor Oliphant a year later. These scientists, working under Lord Rutherford, used directed beams of nuclei to

155

achieve fusion on a minute scale. During the years that followed it was realized that this is the process from which the stars, including our own sun, derive their energy.

What is a Thermo-nuclear Reaction?

When this was understood the scientists may have resigned themselves to the conclusion that Man could never hope to emulate that process on earth; for it takes place only at fantastically high temperatures—hence the term thermo-(heat-) nuclear reaction. In the centre of the sun the temperature is

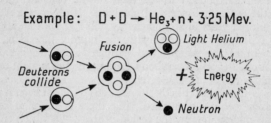

Example: $D + D \rightarrow He_3 + n + 3.25$ Mev.

FIG. 11 Fusion reactions can be produced by making deuterons collide. They form helium nuclei; part of the mass turns into energy in this process, and one neutron escapes in each collision.

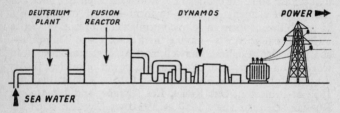

FIG. 12 Scheme of a fusion reactor capable of producing 'power from sea water'.

believed to be about 15 million degrees C although on the outside, which sends us its life-giving rays, it is only 6000° C. In the sun, light elements—mainly ordinary hydrogen—are turned into heavier ones: they are, as it were, 'melted', or fused together. Thus hydrogen nuclei, which consist of one proton each, are fused by the heat into helium nuclei, which have two protons and two neutrons each; during this process

156

some of the mass of the nuclei turns into energy, into heat, and in this way the sun's thermo-nuclear reaction is kept up throughout the ages.

Why does that process require so much heat? Because normally nuclei repel each other, protons being positively charged. If you want them to overcome their repellent force you have to 'bang' them together at great speed. Heat, as we know, is energy, is movement; the greater the heat of any matter the more violent the speed of its particles. Now hydrogen, being the lightest of all elements, has the smallest electrical charge, and therefore its nuclei can be banged together more easily than those of other elements, and this is what the heat achieves. As the hydrogen nuclei collide with each other, some of their mass turns into energy—into heat.

When the atomic bomb became a reality there was, for the first time, the possibility of achieving on earth the necessary high temperatures to start a thermo-nuclear reaction. This has been achieved on a grand and frightening scale in the form of the hydrogen bomb, which uses an 'ordinary' atom bomb as its detonator (see Chapter III). However, as in the case of nuclear fission, the creation of a device for uncontrolled reaction is much simpler than that of a machine for the peaceful utilization of the new source of energy. But thanks to the achievements of a British team of research workers, we are now well on our way to solving mankind's energy problem for all time.

Zeta

The H-bomb reaction has been achieved not with ordinary hydrogen, as in the sun, but with its isotopes deuterium and tritium, which have neutrons as well as protons in their nuclei, and can therefore release more energy. Deuterium has one extra neutron, tritium has two; as the fusion takes place the protons are detached from their electrons, the neutrons break loose, and when they fly off into space they provide extra energy: one of the reasons why the scientists working towards the realization of controlled fusion decided to use hydrogen isotopes instead of natural hydrogen.

Deuterium, or heavy hydrogen, occurs in small proportions in natural hydrogen; tritium occurs in it too, but in still smaller proportions, so that it has to be manufactured artificially if we want to get usable quantities. The oceans of the earth are to all intents and purposes an inexhaustible source of deuterium, and its extraction from water is not too difficult. The fuel cost of thermo-nuclear fusion is therefore negligible, certainly much lower than that of uranium. It has been estimated that one gallon of sea water could yield as much energy as 100 gallons of petrol, and that a bucketful of water containing one-fifth of a gram of deuterium could keep an average house warm for a whole year!

The problem, then, is the economic conversion of that fuel into energy—in other words, the reaction must sustain itself, producing the very high temperatures required, and creating surplus energy for practical use.

This sounds simple, but it is not so easy to reach temperatures of millions of degrees. The use of an atom bomb as in the H-bomb is, of course, ruled out; not only because of its destructive power but also because the heavy hydrogen must be kept hot for longer periods. Before 1950, a temperature of 30,000° C was the highest ever achieved in a laboratory. A special machine was therefore necessary to reach much higher temperatures. That machine was built in Harwell, and its name is ZETA, which stands for 'Zero Energy Thermo-nuclear Assembly' ('Zero Energy' meaning that it is not supposed to produce surplus power for, say, generating electric current).

After two years of design and construction work, ZETA started up in August, 1957. It is, essentially, an aluminium vessel looking like a thick motor-car tyre, measuring about 10 ft across. It is filled with deuterium gas at low pressure (low pressure prevents the machine from blowing up no matter how high the temperature rises inside). When a large electric current is passed through the gas it sets up an electric discharge, not unlike the luminous discharge in a neon advertising sign; this heats the gas to very high temperatures. The current is produced by a huge electromagnet which encircles the tyre. But if the white-hot gas touched the aluminium walls they would just vaporize; therefore the gas must be kept in the centre of the tyre (or torus, as the workers call it). This is done by an intense magnetic field around the gas so that it stays in the centre of the torus without touching the walls.

Dr Peter Thonemann, a young Australian who is responsible for the design of ZETA, achieved this feat—on which the functioning of the whole apparatus depends—by using a phenomenon which Sir George Thomson had been studying since 1946. The electric current, by increasing the attraction of the gas particles towards each other, tends to contract the deuterium and draw it away from the walls into a constricted channel. The gas, of course, resists that 'pinch effect', and some kind of compromise between the opposing forces is reached, but it does stay away from the walls and occupies a narrow channel inside the torus.

If we could look into the torus while the machine is switched on we would not, however, see a steady, brilliantly luminous ring of hot gas. As soon as the current is increased the gas

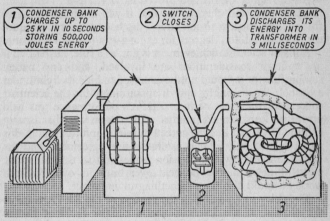

FIG. 13   How ZETA works.

"begins to lash about like an angry snake", as Sir George Thomson put it. The secret of ZETA's success is that this lashing has been reduced to a minimum, and the 'snake' has been kept from vaporizing the walls, up to very high temperatures—up to the crucial point where the thermo-nuclear reaction begins, and neutrons start to fly off from the fused nuclei. This has been done by adding to the natural magnetic field of the current an extra field, produced by coils of wire wound around the torus.

Towards the Thermo-nuclear Power Station

With this assembly, the decisive success was achieved within little more than two weeks after the ZETA switches were thrown for the first time. The temperature was gradually stepped up to 5 million degrees C—higher than the measured surface temperatures of any star; it was kept up only for 2 to 5 thousandths of a second, but during that time neutrons were observed. 'There are good reasons to think that they came from thermo-nuclear reactions,' as the official report put it modestly. A more thorough investigation, however, revealed that these neutrons were not yet genuine fusion products but were due to an unexpected phenomenon—fast deuterons, racing around in the hot gas, must have chipped them off slower ones.

All the same, ZETA had proved its worth as a magnificent research tool, and chances are that it will eventually achieve true thermo-nuclear fusion after it has been rebuilt to produce ten or more million degrees for as long as a tenth of a second.

A major scientific achievement is not, as a rule, hushed up if no military considerations are involved, and any nation responsible for it would not be expected to hide its light under a bushel. Surprisingly, and disappointingly for the scientists concerned, the great news of ZETA's performance was held up for no less than six months. The reason was that Britain and the USA had in 1956 agreed to release information in this research field only after consultation and agreement, and the US Atomic Energy Commission requested that this particular piece of news should be held over until its own research workers would also have something to announce.

The delay in announcing the success of the ZETA team at the request of the USAEC was a unique incident in the history of Science, and must have been an infuriating experience for the men at Harwell. It certainly looked like 'security' gone mad. 'It is being suggested that the United States Atomic Energy Commission is unwilling to stomach publicity for a resounding British achievement at a time when its own reputation in the United States is steadily declining,' explained the *Manchester Guardian* (December 4th, 1957). When the publication on ZETA came at last in January, 1958, it was officially coupled with simultaneous reports by American scientists on their own experiments, and their plans to build a 'super-ZETA', the model C STELLARATOR.

These squabbles and jealousies at the top level of international Science appear rather childish to the outsider, all the more so as the practical utilization of these achievements is

160

still a long way off. "We are now at the same stage as fission research was in 1940 when the possibility of a chain reaction was well understood but many uncertainties remained, and a further 15 years elapsed before large-scale nuclear power was developed," said Sir John Cockcroft in 1957.

But there is no doubt whatsoever that eventually thermonuclear power will be at our disposal, and this means that Man will never have to fear the end of coal and oil supplies, or even a depletion of uranium and thorium deposits. What, then, are the next steps on the road to the thermo-nuclear power station?

Harwell is already designing a much larger version of ZETA, which will be self-sufficient, ie it will produce as much energy as it needs. It will be able to heat the deuterium to temperatures of 100 million degrees C. The temperature is expected to rise quickly with larger currents; ten times as large a current as that used in ZETA might give roughly a hundred times the temperature. 'The step between what is now achieved and what will have to be achieved for the production of a useful supply of power is measured by the difference between 5 million degrees centigrade and 500 million degrees,' wrote Sir George Thomson in 1958, 'but there is reason to believe that the process of further multiplication is now relatively simple. . . . There will no doubt be many difficulties. It will be most unexpected if no unexpected difficulties crop up.'

And it would be equally surprising, one might add, if the next great advance were to come from Britain again, although ZETA is not the only thermo-nuclear research machine in this country. At the Associated Electrical Industries Research Laboratory at Aldermaston, a smaller apparatus called SCEPTRE III, with a 45-in. torus diameter, produced temperatures of nearly 4 million degrees C at which neutrons from some form of nuclear reaction were observed.

But other countries may now forge ahead. The American STELLARATOR will be a most powerful research machine when it is completed in 1961 or thereabouts. In Russia, Professor Kurchatov experiments with straight tubes instead of rings, and the French EQUATOR has already achieved temperatures of one million degrees C. Some research workers in other countries believe that more favourable results could be produced by using tritium as well as deuterium: when their

F

nuclei are 'banged' together and fuse, the result is helium 3, with some neutrons to spare from each reaction. The tritium would not have to be produced by the usual costly process, but could be made in the reactor itself by allowing neutrons from the hot deuterium to be absorbed by a blanket of lithium surrounding the high-temperature region. The neutrons would cause the lithium to disintegrate, and one of the resulting products would be tritium, which is then fed back into the high-temperature region.

Or perhaps mesons may provide the answer to some of the main problems. American scientists have discovered that the fusion of hydrogen isotopes may be brought about by these particles which are found in cosmic rays and have been made artificially in accelerators. The simultaneous collision of a proton, a deuteron (deuterium nucleus), and a certain type of meson may result in the formation of a helium 3 nucleus. Here the difficulty is that mesons have a lifespan of only about one millionth of a second, and that so far they have been produced only in relatively small numbers.

Once we can create surplus energy in a thermo-nuclear reactor, how are we going to utilize it? Sir George Thomson believes that we will not have to use the roundabout way of conducting the heat out of the reactor into heat exchangers and from there to steam turbines as in an 'old-fashioned' atomic power station. "The arrangement by which electric energy is fed into the gas," says Sir George, "may probably be also used to extract energy from it, and turn it into direct electricity. Since this is what one generally wants, and since the efficiency of even a good steam plant, generating electricity, is only about 30 per cent, there is a great possible gain here."

The Atomic Battery

Perhaps the fission process, too, can be utilized to produce electricity by some more direct method than via the steam turbine and the dynamo. As long ago as 1900, Marie and Pierre Curie used radio-activity to produce an electric potential. For fifty years this was regarded merely as a scientific curiosity. Recently, however, American scientists have made some progress on two different lines.

At the General Electric Research Laboratory, Schenectady, a device called a 'thermionic converter' has been developed. It takes advantage of the fact that electrons can be 'boiled out'

162

of a hot metal surface and used to produce an electric current directly. It consists of two electrodes contained in a tube-like vessel; one is kept relatively cool, while the other is heated to a very high temperature. The heat 'boils' electrons, the particles of negative electricity, out of the metal. They enter the space between the two electrodes, which is filled with positively charged particles; the electrons can travel only from the hot to the cool electrode but not back. Thus we get a flow of current which can be conducted out of the vessel to be utilized. If the heat of the hot electrode comes from an atomic reactor we have

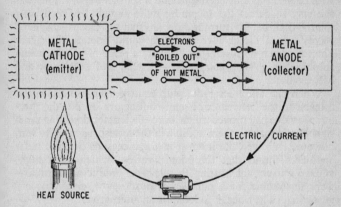

FIG. 14 The 'thermionic converter' for turning nuclear energy directly into electricity.

an assembly for direct conversion of nuclear energy into electricity.

The scientists do not claim that the method is already economically feasible; they have not achieved more than an 8 per cent conversion of heat into current, and believe that this could be stepped up to 30 per cent. However, it is a beginning.

The other method was demonstrated in 1954 by Mr David Sarnoff, of the Radio Corporation of America. He showed the Press a little box connected by wires with a telegraph key on the one hand and with an earphone on the other. When he pressed the key there was an audible tone in the earphone. The energy which produced it came from the little box, the 'atomic battery'. To understand the way in which it works—

and how the 'atomic watch' functions, which is another experimental development—we have to explain a modern scientific miracle, the transistor.

The transistor is another brilliant achievement of the period after the Second World War, although its development goes back to the early days of radio. Those of us who are old enough will remember that we sat listening to the magic sounds coming through space with headphones clamped over our ears, fiddling about with crystal detectors—'cat's whiskers' was the nickname for the fine little wires which we had to adjust on the surface of a piece of crystal to find a sensitive spot. This was the way to detect the incoming radio signals by 'rectifying' them—that is, by turning the alternating electro-magnetic waves into a direct current which could operate the headphones. Such a crystal (then usually a piece of galena, a lead sulphide) is a 'semi-conductor'—that is, half conductor and half insulator.

When the amplifier radio with loudspeaker came into use interest in the behaviour of semi-conductors lapsed; the thermionic valve had proved much more efficient for detecting radio signals and making them audible in the loudspeaker. The war, however, renewed the interest in these crystals because radar engineers found that thermionic valves—which need high-voltage current for heating the electron-producing cathode—were unsuitable for a number of purposes in electronic engineering. They began to look for an alternative.

In 1948 scientists of the Bell Telephone Laboratories demonstrated their first transistor. Without going into technical details, fascinating though they are, it may be sufficient to say that a transistor does the job of a thermionic valve—it controls electrons. It consists of a piece of germanium or silicon, which are semi-conductors; by introducing certain 'impurities' into the crystal it is made into a kind of miniature racecourse for electrons. If an incoming radio signal (or a signal from a deaf-aid microphone, a gramophone pick-up, etc.) injects, say, 1 million electrons into the crystal, 50 million electrons will start to flow in a closed circuit. The result is that amplification is achieved with a minimum of power; in fact, you can operate a loudspeaker radio with transistors instead of valves for a year or so on a torch battery!

This miraculous little gadget, which is shorter than a matchstick and not much thicker, is already in use for a large number of purposes, from portable radios to guided missiles, and from electronic brains to automatic garage doors. And it can be used for converting atomic energy directly into electricity.

The RCA battery demonstrated in 1954 consists of a thin disc of strontium 90, the radio-active isotope, no more than 1/300 of a cubic centimetre, in contact with a transistor wafer. The isotope bombards the wafer with several billion electrons per second, releasing many more electrons in it. In fact, some 200,000 electrons are released for each electron from the isotope. The result is a minute amount of electric current, just enough to produce a tone in an earphone.

The early RCA model was no more than a first step. After some time of operation it was found that there was a certain amount of disintegration in the transistor wafer. Besides, strontium 90 needs too much shielding, being a potentially dangerous radiation source.

A British model of the atomic battery uses promethium 147 instead, atomic number 61. It gives off electrons which strike a small quantity of phosphorus powder of a type used in fluorescent light tubes. The powder begins to glow, and the light falls on a minute silicon wafer which acts as a photo-electric cell, converting the light into electric current. No electrons are allowed to escape. This device produces about 20 microwatts power. Only light shielding is necessary.

The atomic watch is the first practical application of an atomic battery. Its 'energizer', as the tiny battery is called, consists of a multi-layer sandwich with a mixture of promethium 147 and phosphorus in the centre. The radiation from this source falls on two layers of silicon, one on either side of the centre layer. The silicon acts as a photo-electric cell, and the resulting current goes into the minute electric motor which drives the watch. A thin metal shield around the 'energizer' is sufficient to prevent the radiation from penetrating the wearer's skin; the promethium emits only electrons which cannot do much harm anyway. Swiss firms are paying a good deal of attention to this development, but they are not yet convinced that the nuclear-powered watch is superior to the self-winding types which have been on the market for many years.

However, the combination of radio-active source and transistor seems to point to a most important possible development. It may be that, as Mr Sarnoff predicts, atomic batteries will be commonplace long before 1980, installed in homes and industrial plants, providing power for years without recharging; it may even be that nuclear-power stations will ultimately discard their heat exchangers, their steam-turbines and generators to produce current directly from radiation.

Another practical use made of the same principle is the atomic lamp, which has been developed by European and American laboratories, and which may be capable of working for twelve years without refuelling. It works with the radioactive gas, krypton 85, enclosed in a chamber; its radiation is converted into visible light when the particles fall on the phosphorus-crystals which coat the inside of the lens. The colour of the light can be chosen and changed at will; this is done by sending the radiation beam through specially coated lenses. The atomic lamp might be useful where low-intensity lighting is required but no electricity available. It has also been suggested to use it for permanent signals along the railway lines and in mines because it cannot cause an explosion.

Remodelling the Earth?

We have already discussed a few of the ambitious schemes which might be carried out when atomic power supplies us with an abundance of energy—for example, the irrigation of Australia's arid regions coupled with the production of fresh water from sea water. On a smaller scale, some islands, such as Bermuda, which is continually short of fresh water, would also benefit from projects of this kind. On a larger scale, however, there is almost no limit to the things Man could do to improve his planet.

Some years ago the Russians reported that they had carried out a major irrigation scheme, involving the blowing-up of a mountain and the reversal of the direction of flow of a river in Southern Siberia, with the help of atomic explosions. Provided the problem of radiation risks can be solved, nuclear charges might indeed be used like dynamite and TNT, which they would surpass by far in explosive power. They might be able to stimulate artificially submarine volcanic eruptions which would throw up new islands in the ocean—another Soviet idea which they intend to apply in the Arctic. Sir Raymond Priestley, the British scientist, has suggested the use of nuclear energy in the Antarctic: "If atomic icebreakers can be built, why not atomic-powered settlements on the Antarctic mainland?" These colonies should establish a great mining industry: "Once the ore is located the whole enterprise could go underground. Tunnel or adit entry might be followed by the construction of underground engine rooms, hoisting gear, and mineral dressing plants. Floating power stations that could be withdrawn during the 'closed' season might be a useful expedient in the initial stages."

Someone might also hit on the idea of making mining in the Antarctic easier by melting the snow and ice cover with a number of fission or fusion bombs. We can only hope that the risk they will be taking with it will be calculated because huge masses of molten ice and snow could produce dangerous tidal waves, and radio-active products would poison the water and the atmosphere.

Why should we not remodel the Earth once we have satisfied people's most urgent needs everywhere? We could use nuclear energy to pump the warm waters of the Pacific into the Arctic Ocean; one year's pumping would impart to the Arctic waters as much warmth as 10 billion tons of oil could supply. The result would be a new Gulf Stream warming up northern Canada and Siberia, making them as habitable as northern Norway is today thanks to the existing Gulf Stream.

No less ambitious is another favourite project of the Earth remodellers, the creation of two enormous seas in the midst of Africa to change the whole climate and ecology of that continent. This, too, can only be done when enormous power supplies become available. The jungle and desert areas of Africa's interior could thus be turned into pleasant and fertile land for settlement and farming in a process taking thirty to fifty years. It would, of course, require the organizational, administrative, and financial cooperation of a number of nations—perhaps a world planning authority.

And if mankind wants to make up for land lost to the waters of the African seas there is always the Mediterranean to fall back upon. With the help of nuclear power the thirty-year-old plan of a German engineer, Hermann Sörgel, might be carried out. He suggested the restoration of the Mediterranean as it must have been about 50,000 years ago: with three wide isthmuses connecting Europe and Africa—from present-day Spain to Morocco, from Italy and Sicily to Tunisia, and from Greece and Crete to Libya. The level of the Mediterranean was roughly 3000 ft lower than it is now. But already the lowering of the sea level by 660 ft in the eastern half and by

330 ft in the western half of the Mediterranean would produce fantastic results—adding 50 or 100 miles to the depth of the coasts, connecting the Greek islands by a new mass of land, drying up the Adriatic, and turning Corsica and Sardinia into one island. All this could be done mainly by building three dams: at Gibraltar, across the Dardanelles, and from Sicily to Tunisia. However, great as the gain in fertile land may be, one can foresee a good many objections to this ambitious scheme, from admirals as well as from Riviera hotel-keepers.

In the more immediate future mining by means of nuclear explosions may provide a short cut to not easily accessible mineral deposits. Professor Libby, of the US Atomic Energy Commission, reported in 1957 that a test explosion had been made in Nevada. A 1900-ft tunnel was drilled into a mountain, and a fission bomb set off in it. The mountain jumped 12 in. into the air; masses of rock melted, and one side of the mountain caved in, revealing the mineral deposits inside. The same technique, says Professor Libby, may be used to build new harbours.

Space Travel by Nuclear Rocket

From the earliest days of atomic research space travel by nuclear rocket has been a foregone conclusion in the minds of the general public. Yet the fact remains that the first sputniks were propelled into their orbits by chemical fuels, which proved sufficiently powerful to provide the necessary escape velocity—the speed which a rocket must reach if we want it to coast around the Earth—and only a little more energy is necessary to pull a space missile out of the orbit on its trip to the Moon. If a chemical rocket can attain the fantastic speed of 18,000 or 20,000 mph, why should we bother about nuclear propulsion for spaceships?

The answer is that a journey to the Moon, which a chemical rocket can achieve, will only serve to whet Man's appetite for 'true' space travel, meaning a trip to Mars or Venus to start with. And these are places which he can never reach without nuclear propulsion. Besides, a manned expedition even to the Moon requires energies which nuclear reactions alone can provide.

It has been estimated that the first two atom bombs liberated some 10 million mile-tons of energy, more than enough to take a mass of 1000 tons to the Moon and back. Fifty pounds of nuclear fuel did a job which would have required millions of tons of chemicals. Even before the possibility of nuclear propulsion in space travel was ever envisaged, the absurdity of carrying enormous masses of fuel out of the Earth's gravitational field was realized, and the idea of a large artificial satellite was born—a space station serving as a kind of celestial petrol pump where spaceships would get their fuel, or perhaps where the travellers bound for other planets would have to change from a small shuttle rocket which had brought them up from the Earth to a large interplanetary ship. Even so, spaceships using chemical fuels would have to consist of 75–90 per cent fuel. Atomic energy would reduce the fuel weight quite substantially.

But here the problem is that of machinery. A rocket ship is propelled by the recoil principle based on Newton's third law of motion: that to every action there is an equal and opposite reaction. By shooting out matter the spaceship pushes itself forward. But how can nuclear energy produce and shoot out matter? And how can these products of atomic reactions be 'beamed' into one direction?

'Direct' utilization of nuclear energy in the form of a jet seems, therefore, extremely difficult, and we have to consider some more complicated way of using the heat produced in atomic reactions. The obvious system would be some kind of adaptation of the thermal reactor, in which the heat produced in the pile is converted into mechanical power by means of heat exchangers and turbines. In the atomic rocket we could transfer the reactor heat to some propellant fluid—perhaps water, which would be ejected as steam; but then we would need masses of it, and we do not want to carry large quantities of fluids into space.

How, then, about a rocket in which the heat is not transferred from the reactor to the propellant, but liberated inside the latter? In this case the nuclear fuel would have to be mixed with the propellant. But this means that nuclear fuel would be lost into space together with the propellant, which would mean a waste; besides, only those fluids which do not absorb too many neutrons could be used, and these may not have the best qualities as propellants.

For all these reasons, spaceship engineers have turned to what is termed the 'ion rocket'. An ion, as we know, is an atom or group of atoms which have become electrically charged;

positive ions have fewer electrons than electrically neutral ones, negative ions have an excess of electrons. Thus the proton, the hydrogen nucleus without its electron, is a hydrogen ion; the alpha particle, consisting of two protons and two neutrons, is a helium ion.

In any laboratory experiment the energy produced by ionization of atoms is minute, but rocket engineers believe that they can develop an engine with an ion exhaust of terrific thrust. Heavy particles of high atomic weight would be the most suitable ones, and it has been estimated that an exhaust velocity of 100 km (62 miles) per second could be produced by an electrostatic field of 10,000 volts. If, for instance, mercury were used as a source of ionized atoms, only 1 gm of it would be consumed per second per ton of rocket mass.

This sounds attractive, but the ion rocket is not a simple piece of machinery. It needs a fission reactor which produces electricity by the usual roundabout way—coolant with or without heat exchanger, gas or steam turbine, generator. However, the whole combination could be kept relatively small and compact. The generator is required to create an accelerating electrostatic field and maintain a current of ions across it. The reactor supplies the fission fragments which are turned into ions.

Side by side with the ion rocket, the electron rocket has been suggested by some spaceship enthusiasts. It would not need an electric generator, but derive its kinetic energy from fast-travelling electrons. So far, electrons have not been found to be very suitable for thrust—their mass is so very small. However, there is a well-known laboratory experiment showing that they have some pushing power: a tiny mica wheel is driven inside a cathode-ray tube by the stream of electrons. From here it is, admittedly, a long way to the spaceship.

Then there is the idea of the alpha rocket, which uses some radio-active substance as a source of alpha particles. Normally they are emitted in all directions, but they could be 'beamed' by large plane surfaces mounted at right angles to the flight path—not unlike the sails of a ship—and coated with the radio-active material. The recoiling alpha particles would form an exhaust stream; those emitted forwards or sideways would be absorbed by the 'sails', with resulting dissipation of heat. The drawback is that half the total energy released would become waste heat, but the designers might find a way of utilizing it.

The problem of weight is, of course, the over-riding one. It is not only the machinery which has to be considered from this point of view, but also the shielding. In a manned rocket of the usual elongated shape the shielding could be kept down to a minimum as only the radio-active parts would have to be fenced off along the breadth of the vehicle. Still, this is a major engineering problem, and it will be necessary to weigh the advantages and disadvantages of, say, a fast-neutron reactor, which is lighter, but needs thicker shielding, against those of a thermal reactor, whose weight is greater but which requires less shielding. If the rocket engineers were satisfied with exhaust velocities of 15 km (9·3 miles) per second, which would be sufficient for a trip to the Moon (and back), the system offering the best weight-energy ratio would be that in which a reactor heats the propellant, water or hydrogen, which then forms the exhaust jet; the above-mentioned difficulty of having to carry the propellant up into space could be solved by using the method of 'all change' at the space station. The trip from the Earth to the space station might be accomplished by using chemical propellants.

This would also solve the problem involved in starting from the Earth by means of a jet containing radio-active particles, which would constitute a danger for organic life in a wide radius.

So many questions remain to be answered and so many difficulties seem to beset the spaceship constructors that the outlook for manned trips to the planets does not appear to be very bright. But if we look up the history of the aeroplane we find that in the early 1920s even the experts were still convinced that there would never be any transatlantic flying as the aeroplane could not cover distances of over 1000 miles non-stop, and that speeds of more than 150 mph were impossible. Today these opinions seem rather ridiculous. They have been disproved not only by new inventions such as the jet engine, but by a long series of minor improvements—new light alloys, variable-pitch propeller blades, streamlined design, and so on. Similar developments may be expected in space travel. Thousands of scientists and constructors are working on the problems involved; at the Los Alamos research station alone no less than 120 workers are engaged in these studies. As usual, military considerations provide the main spur, but it is perhaps not too sanguine to hope that the first expedition to Mars or Venus from the Earth may be a peaceful international venture, not a race between, say, America and Russia to be there first and claim possession of the planet in question.

But how could we really travel to some other planet of our solar system, to say nothing of journeys to other solar systems? Speeds of 110,000–140,000 mph are necessary to reach Mars or Venus, make a landing, and return to Earth. It seems improbable that any of the rocket systems which we have discussed can provide the necessary energy. But the scientists have already another idea up their sleeves; it is the photon rocket.

The photon is a quantum of radiant energy, or the 'particle' of light just as the electron is the particle of electricity. But there is a fundamental difference. Electrons have some mass, though very little; light, like other electromagnetic radiations, travels through space as a wave motion. However, this is not a continuous motion; it takes place in the form of infinitesimal 'bursts' of energy, of quanta, whose 'size' depends on the wavelength, or frequency of radiation. The photon is, therefore, not a real particle, but such a minute, yet finite, quantum of light, and although it is only electromagnetic energy it interacts with matter as if it were a particle of mass. Its speed, the velocity of light, is 186,000 miles a second; and as velocity is energy the idea of using the photon as a source of energy for propelling spaceships is only logical.

It is a fact that the sunlight exerts a measurable pressure on the Earth. Because of the diffusion of light it is extremely small, but if it were possible to concentrate photon pressure into a narrow beam it might produce the thrust necessary for space travel, propelling the astronautical vehicle with a velocity approaching that of light.

The problem of how to produce photons—those released by the sun cannot be 'caught' and utilized for the purpose—has been solved, if only in theory. You take one electron and one positron (a positively charged electron) and make them annihilate each other mutually. This results in their masses being completely converted into energy in the form of two photons; they would, however, shoot off in opposite directions.

The sceptics among the scientists hold that even if this complete conversion of mass into electromagnetic energy were possible and the photons could be made to go in the same

172

direction, there would not be enough acceleration produced to send the photon rocket soaring away into outer space, and a trip even to the nearest star would take centuries. Among the believers, however, is a Russian scientist, Professor K. A. Gilzin, who declares that according to Einstein's theory of de-acceleration the space travellers would live much longer than those they left behind on Earth, provided the velocity of their photon rocket approaches the speed of light.

With this notion he chimes in with some of the speakers at the International Astronautical Congress in Rome in 1956, who delighted in the idea that travellers in space would be cheating Death by a number of years if their journey were long and fast enough. Sir George Thomson, too, wrote that during a trip to the nearest star and back, taking seventeen years according to our telluric time-table, the travellers would age only fourteen and a half years. The argument was taken up and hotly discussed by some British scientists in a lengthy exchange of letters in *Nature*.

Professor Gilzin, however, is not satisfied with saving a measly two and a half years. Travellers staying away for half their lifetime, he wrote in an article in *Soviet Aviation* in 1958, would discover on their return that thousands of years had passed on earth. The Professor is confident that the Soviet Union, which made the first step into space with her sputniks, will build such a photon rocket, which would not carry any fuel, but pick up all the particles of matter it encounters in space and transform them into electromagnetic energy. The ship would be of enormous size, consisting of four huge rectangles, each two-fifths of a square mile in area. There would be a passenger cabin in the centre, and here the space travellers would lead a life as near as possible to what they were used to on Earth.

Those who dare to entrust themselves to such a space-time machine will need a good deal of faith—faith in Science, in their crew, in Professor Gilzin's judgment, and in mankind in general. What would they find when they return from their journey after thousands of earthly years? Even if we stretch our imagination as far as thought can reach we cannot foretell how people will live in that distant future. We do not even know if mankind will outlast our own century.

GLOSSARY OF THE ATOMIC AGE

Accelerator: Machine for imparting very high speeds to atomic particles by electric or magnetic forces. Two main types: the linear accelerator, which is essentially a long tube, and the cyclotron (*qv*). *See also* Meson.

Alpha Particle: Nucleus (*qv*) of a helium atom without its electrons, therefore positively charged. Streams of alpha rays are given off by many radio-active substances.

Atom: The smallest particle of an element which retains the characteristics of the element. It has a massive central nucleus carrying a positive electric charge and consisting of a definite number of protons, neutrons and other particles (mesons) whose nature is still under investigation; around the nucleus move a number of electrons (*qv*) in orbits at relatively great distances. Normally the number of electrons corresponds to that of the protons in the nucleus; thus the electric charges cancel each other out and the atom is neutral. *See also* Ionization.

Atomic Energy: The energy released when the nucleus of a heavy atom is chipped or split by colliding with a neutron or another particle (*see* Fission). A minute part of the nucleus changes completely into energy. *See also* Fusion.

Atomic Number: The number of protons in the atomic nucleus (*qv*) and the corresponding number of electrons (*qv*). This number distinguishes one element from another by determining its chemical properties.

Atomic Pile: A nuclear reactor (*qv*) having a graphite moderator (*qv*).

Atomic Weight: Average weight of the atoms of an element expressed on a scale in which the weight of an oxygen element is 16 and that of a hydrogen element almost exactly 1.

Beta Particle: An electron (*qv*) when emitted as radiation.

Breeder Reactor: A nuclear reactor (*qv*) producing more nuclear fuel than it consumes; natural uranium or thorium is changed into enriched fuel (*qv*) such as plutonium or a uranium isotope (*qv*).

Chain Reaction: The 'burning' reaction in a nuclear reactor (*qv*) by which the neutrons released from split nuclei hit other nuclei, splitting them and thereby releasing more neutrons, together with energy in the form of heat and fragments (fission products), and so on.

Core: The inner part of a nuclear reactor (*qv*) containing the atomic fuel and the moderator (*qv*).

Cosmic Rays: Penetrating particles (*eg* mesons, *qv*) reaching the Earth from outer space.

Critical Mass: The smallest mass of fissile material (atomic fuel) in which a chain reaction can be maintained.

Crystal: A piece of matter of regular shape in which the atoms are arranged in a repeating pattern.

Curie: The unit used for measuring radio-activity. One curie = activity from about 40,000 million atoms breaking up every second.

Cyclotron: A machine for accelerating atomic particles to high speeds, thereby increasing their energy by means of giving them 'pushes' in strong electric or magnetic fields. It has a circular shape. *See also* Accelerator. The instrument is used for research work in which atoms are bombarded and 'smashed'. Other forms are the bevatron, synchrotron, etc.

Electron: The smallest atomic particle and the lightest component of matter. It is the fundamental element of electricity, usually with a negative charge; but there are also positive electrons called positrons. *See also* Beta Particle.

Element: One of the basic substances of which the universe is built. There are 92 elements occurring in Nature. *See also* Atomic Number.

Enriched Fuel: Usually meaning natural uranium to which extra quantities of a fissile uranium isotope or plutonium have been added.

Fast Reactor: A nuclear reactor in which fissions are caused by neutrons moving at their original high speeds, not having been slowed down by a moderator (*qv*).

Fission: The disintegration of atomic nuclei in a chain reaction (*qv*) when hit by neutrons, a process by which neutrons and energy are released.

Fusion: The 'melting together' of two atoms of low atomic weight, *eg* heavy hydrogen (deuterium) or triple heavy hydrogen (tritium), both hydrogen isotopes (*qv*). Fusion produced by high temperatures is also called thermo-nuclear reaction.

Gamma Radiation: Electro-magnetic radiation similar to X-rays, produced when certain nuclei disintegrate. It is extremely penetrating and potentially dangerous.

Geiger Counter: Instrument for detecting and counting alpha, beta, and gamma radiation (*qv*). This is done by making them pass through a gas in which they produce ionization (*qv*).

Half-life: The time taken by a radio-active substance to decay to half its original activity.

Heavy Elements: Elements with great atomic weights (*qv*) such as uranium (238), thorium (232), or radium (226).

Heavy Hydrogen: An isotope (*qv*) of hydrogen, deuterium, or tritium, in which the nucleus has greater weight because of the presence of one or two neutrons beside the proton (*qv*).

Heavy Water: Water formed by heavy hydrogen (*qv*) and oxygen.

Ionization: Ions are electrically charged atoms; their electrical balance has been disturbed by the removal of one or more electrons. *See* also Atom. Ionization is the formation of such atoms.

Isotope: Atom of an element which is identical in its chemical properties but has different atomic weight and physical (nuclear) properties, usually because of the presence of one or more extra neutrons in the nucleus, or because of the absence of some of the neutrons found in the common form of the element. Most elements occurring in Nature are mixtures of a common form and one or more rarer isotopes.

Meson: Unstable atomic particle found in cosmic rays (*qv*), with a mass between that of an electron and a proton. The meson is now believed to be the 'atomic glue' holding the nucleus together. It can be made artificially by an accelerator (*qv*).

Moderator: Material (*eg* graphite) used in a nuclear reactor (*qv*) to slow down the neutrons produced by fission so that they are not absorbed, or 'captured', by the nuclei they encounter, but split them.

Molecule: Combination of atoms of one or several elements; the smallest part of a substance capable of existing independently while retaining the properties of the original substance (*eg* water, salt, sugar, starch, etc.).

Neutrino: Sub-atomic uncharged particle whose existence has been assumed to explain nuclear reactions according to the basic laws of 'conservation of mass and energy'.

Neutron: An atomic particle which has no electric charge, found in the nucleus. It is the sub-atomic 'bullet' which causes nuclear fission (*qv*).

Nucleus: The central part of the atom (*qv*) containing most of its mass. It is always positively charged.

Proton: Basic particle of the atomic nucleus. It carries a positive electric charge.

Radio-Activity: The spontaneous disintegration of atoms of certain elements, accompanied by emission of alpha, beta, or gamma rays (*qv*).

Reactor: The 'furnace' in which nuclear fission produces heat. Most reactors consist of a core (*qv*) containing the fuel elements, the moderator (*qv*), and the control rods; the coolant, a liquid or gas which carries the heat out of the core, circulates through it. Graphite-moderated reactors are also called piles.

Thermo-Nuclear Reaction: *see* Fusion.

Tracers: Radio-active atoms of isotopes, used in small quantities for tracing, by their radiation, the path through a living organism of some substance to which they are attached.

Transuranic Elements: Elements, not found in Nature but artificially produced, of higher weight than uranium (*eg* plutonium).

X-Rays: Electro-magnetic waves of very short wavelengths and great power of penetration, capable of destroying living tissues. *See also* Gamma Radiation.

CAREERS IN ATOMIC RESEARCH AND ENGINEERING

The Need for Scientists and Technicians

Britain lags numerically very much behind the Soviet Union and the United States in scientific and technical education. Russia turns out 280 engineering and science graduates per million people each year, America 136, Britain only 57. Britain has established herself as the leading nation in the peaceful applications of atomic energy; but she cannot keep the pace without a substantial influx of skilled technologists. The development of her nuclear industry requires a major switch from unskilled to skilled labour and from the arts and humanities to science and engineering.

The prospects for young people with interest and abilities in these fields are excellent. "There is no dearth of potential scientists in the ranks of the new generation," said one of Britain's leading physicists. "We have only to look at the hordes of Walter Mittys who travel through outer space in their imagination. Many of them could be on their way to becoming real scientists if they had met an inspired teacher. Then they would know about the excitement of discovering the ways of Nature, and would not waste their time with the inanities of popular science fiction."

This does not mean that languages are a waste of schooltime. "You will be glad of your extra language when travelling or attending scientific conferences," said Sir John Cockcroft in an address to young people in 1957. "And when you are struggling to write up a year's work for publication or writing a paper to convince your colleagues or bosses that they should pursue ideas based on your work you will find that the English essay and your English reading of literature was a good preparation for this."

The United Kingdom Atomic Energy Authority has urgent need of scientific workers, experimental officers, scientific assistants, engineers and other technical staff. It runs an apprenticeship scheme for training in engineering (electrical and electronic, or mechanical, and chemical, or physics) and in metallurgy. It provides an all-round education, and there are splendid opportunities for those who have the ability and aptitude to gain experience in research and development work.

Apprentices are trained at the following establishments:

Atomic Energy Research Establishment, Harwell, Berks.
Atomic Weapons Research Establishment, Aldermaston, Berks.
[1]Radiochemical Centre, Amersham, Bucks.
Capenhurst Works, Capenhurst, Chester
[1]Springfield Works, Salwick, Preston
Calder Works and Windscale Works, Sellafield, Cumberland
[1]Dounreay Works, Caithness
[1]Atomic Weapons Research Establishment, Woolwich, London

Craft apprentices are recruited at sixteen years of age by the Apprenticeship Board of the AEA. Selected boys may enter at fifteen as pre-apprentice learners. Apprenticeship is normally completed on reaching the age of twenty-one years. Among the crafts in which they are trained in the first year are tool and gauge maker, instrument maker, electrician, sheet metal worker, fitter, electronic mechanic, etc.

Student apprentices are accepted at the ages of sixteen to eighteen and a half years, and recruited by a Central Selection Board. Qualifications include a General Certificate of Education with passes at ordinary or advanced level in at least four subjects, three of which must be mathematics, physics, and General Science.

After at least one year of workshop training, selected student apprentices who have satisfied university entrance requirements may be given the opportunity to attend a full-time university course leading to an honours degree in mechanical, electrical, or chemical engineering or metallurgy.

Each year a post-graduate scholarship may be awarded to a fifth-year student apprentice so that he can undertake advanced study or research in a university or institute.

All applications should be made to the Chief Labour Officer, United Kingdom Atomic Energy Authority, Bedford Chambers, Covent Garden, London WC2, for student apprenticeships and pre-graduate apprenticeships. Craft apprentices are recruited locally; information and advice may be obtained from the Local Youth Employment Officer.

Careers in Research, Development, and Construction

The Industrial Group of the AEA, whose headquarters is at Risley, Warrington, Lancs., has especially interesting work for university graduates and trained scientists, men as well as

---

[1] Craft Apprentices only.

women. They are offered more than jobs—they are offered careers.

Graduates in chemistry are appointed to undertake work as professional or plant chemists, analytical chemists, or research chemists.

For physicists the scope and variety of work in the Industrial Group is practically unlimited, ranging from reactor physics, electronics, health physics and irradiation physics to the economic assessment of future projects. Mathematicians are employed at Risley and in all the laboratories.

Graduate engineers are required to have served an apprenticeship, or to show that they have practical experience. There are careers for design engineers, research and development engineers, works engineers, construction engineers, and chemical engineers.

Metallurgists are employed at Harwell, at the Research and Development Laboratories at Culcheth (near Risley), Springfields, Aldermaston, Dounreay and Windscale; graduates are eligible for appointment as Scientific Officers, Assistant Experimental Officers, or Professional Metallurgists.

All applications should be made to the Recruitment Section, UK Atomic Energy Authority, Industrial Group HQ, Risley, Warrington, Lancs.

Reactor School and Isotope School

The Atomic Energy Authority runs three 'schools'. The Reactor School at Harwell trains qualified students from industry and from overseas countries in the science and engineering of nuclear power stations in four courses held every year, each lasting sixteen weeks; there are also special courses for senior industrialists with a technical background, each lasting ten days, giving an overall appreciation of the problems of reactor technology.

Complementary to the Harwell Reactor School there is the Calder Operations School at Calder Hall, where students receive theoretical and practical instruction in the operation of the Calder Hall type of reactors. These courses last six weeks each.

The Isotope School at Harwell was opened in 1951. It has a standard four-weeks course and some specialized and advanced courses on subjects such as radiological protection, autoradiography, and the medical uses of radio-isotopes.

The new Rutherford Institute for Nuclear Research at Harwell offers very important work to young post-graduate scientists.

Atomic Power Groups in Industry

There are now several large groups in Britain's industry co-operating in the atomic engineering field. The most important of them—all of which are looking for scientific and technological staff—are the following:

The General Electric Co.—Simon Carves Industrial Atomic Energy Group. (Address: Atomic Energy Dept., G.E.C., Fraser Chalmers Engineering Works, Erith, Kent)

Nuclear Power Plant Co. Ltd. (McAlpine, Parsons, Whessoe, Head Wrightson, Findlay and other companies). (Address: Nuclear Power Plant Co. Ltd., Booths Hall, Knutsford, Cheshire)

Atomic Power Projects Ltd. (English Electric, Babcock & Wilcox, and Taylor Woodrow). (Address: Atomic Power Dept., The English Electric Co. Ltd., Whetstone, nr. Leicester)

A.E.I.—John Thompson Nuclear Energy Co. Ltd. (Associated Electrical Industries, Metropolitan-Vickers, British Thomson-Houston and others). (Address: Industrial Nuclear Energy Group, A.E.I. & John Thompson, Oak House, Cross St, Sale, Cheshire)

Atomic Power Constructions Ltd. (Richardsons Westgarth, International Combustion, Crompton Parkinson and others). (Address: Atomic Power Constructions Ltd., 28–30 Theobalds Road, London WC1)

AMF-MEL Atomics—International Nuclear Power Associates (Mitchell Engineering, AMF Atomics, New York, and Nuclear Construction Ltd.). (Address: Mitchell Engineering Ltd., Nuclear Power Division, 1 Bedford Square, London WC1)

BOOKS AND FILMS ON NUCLEAR ENERGY

Bibliographies on atomic energy in general and some of its special aspects are prepared by the UK Atomic Energy Authority from time to time. They can be obtained through HM Stationery Office, through booksellers, and from some public libraries. Copies of many books and documents on atomic energy can be borrowed from the following libraries:

> Science Museum Library, South Kensington, London SW7
> Central Library, Surrey Street, Sheffield 1
> Central Library, Ratcliffe Place, Birmingham 1
> The Mitchell Library, North Street, Glasgow 3
> Central Library, William Brown Street, Liverpool 3
> Central Library, St Peter's Square, Manchester 2
> Central Library, New Bridge Street, Newcastle-upon-Tyne 1
> Central Library, High Street, Acton, London W3
> Central Library, Albion Street, Kingston-upon-Hull

Selected Reading List

BERTIN, L. *Atom Harvest* (Secker & Warburg, 1955)

COCKCROFT, Sir John D. *The Development and Future of Atomic Energy* (Clarendon Press, Oxford, 1950)
The Industrial Challenge of Nuclear Energy (published by the Organization for European Economic Co-operation, Paris 16)

ADAMS, M. 'Atom Harbour: The Story of Dounreay' (Steel Review 2, *British Iron & Steel Federation Quarterly*, April 1956)

JAY, K. E. B. *Calder Hall* (Methuen & Co., 1956)

UK Atomic Energy Authority. *Atom 1956* (HM Stationery Office, 1956)

Ministry of Supply. *Harwell 1946–1951* (HM Stationery Office, 1952)

CRAMMER, J. L. and PEIERLS, R. E. *Atomic Energy* (Penguin Science News No 2 and Pelican Book No A224. 1950)

HALLOWS, R. W. *Atoms and Atomic Energy* (Chapman & Hall, 1950)

182

JAY, K. E. B. *Atomic Energy Research at Harwell* (Butterworth, 1955)

ROWLAND, John. *Atoms Work Like This* (Phoenix House, 1955)

JONES, G. O., ROTBLAT, J., and WHITROW, G. J. *Atoms and the Universe* (Eyre & Spottiswoode, 1956)

THOMPSON, Sir George. *The Atom* (Oxford University Press, 1956)

BLACKETT, P. M. S. *Atomic Weapons and East–West Relations* (Cambridge University Press, 1956)

BRONOWSKI, J. *The Atom* (Newman Neame Take Home Books, 1956)

RADCLIFFE, A. and ROBINSON, E. C. *The True Book about Atomic Energy* (Frederick Muller, 1955)

TITTERTON, E. W. *Facing the Atomic Future* (Macmillan, 1956)

Periodicals

Atoms for Peace Digest (United States Information Service, London W1)

Atom (Monthly Bulletin of the UK Atomic Energy Authority)

Atom Industry (132–134 Fleet St, London EC4)

Applied Atomics (Reuters, London EC4)

Atomics and Nuclear Energy (London, Leonard Hill Technical Group)

Journal of Nuclear Energy (London, Pergamon Press Ltd.)

Nuclear Power: Journal of British Nuclear Engineering (London, Rowse Muir)

Nuclear Engineering (London, Temple Press Ltd.)

Journal of the British Nuclear Energy Conference (London)

Sections on nuclear energy are found regularly in *The New Scientist*, *Discovery*, *Engineering*, and *The Engineer*

Films

There are large numbers of documentary, training, teaching, and background films on atomic energy available in the United Kingdom. A full list of 145 films was published in October, 1956, as a special issue of the *Scientific Film Review*; this is obtainable from the Editorial Office of the Scientific Film Association, 164 Shaftesbury Avenue, London WC2, at 3*s* 6*d*. The major sources of films for hire are the following:

Central Office of Information Film Library, Government Buildings, Bromyard Avenue, Acton, London W3

Gaumont British Film Library, 1 Aintree Road, Perivale, Greenford, Middlesex

Ace Distributors Ltd., 14 Broadwick St, London W1

Foundation Film Library, Brooklands House, Weybridge, Surrey

United States Information Service, American Embassy, Grosvenor Square, London W1

Contemporary Films, 14 Soho Square, London W1

Plato Films (Soviet documentaries), 18 Greek St, London W1

French Embassy, Cultural Counsellor, 22 Wilton Crescent, London SW1

Sound-Services Ltd., 269 Kingston Road, London SW19

INDEX

189

WAR IN THE AIR

Gerald Bowman

NEWSPAPERMAN and ex-Squadron Leader Gerald Bowman has based this book on the immensely popular series of fifteen television films made by the BBC, for which Air Chief Marshal Sir Philip Joubert, KCB, CMG, DSO (who writes a Foreword to the book) was Technical Adviser.

Here, told compactly, is the story of the tremendous air power developed during the Second World War by the Allies—from puny beginnings to the Atomic Bomb. The final chapters, specially rewritten for this edition, focus on the future, outlining the part that air power is likely to play in world affairs in view of the nuclear bomb, intercontinental ballistic missiles, etc. A special Appendix gives full details of representative aircraft engaged in both World Wars.

Fully indexed and with four pages of illustrations in photogravure. (2/6)

THE PAN BOOK OF
CROSSWORDS

Compiled by

L. W. Burgess

HERE is a book of really *popular* crosswords. After a quarter of a century's experience in providing crosswords for the leading newspapers and periodicals of this country, Mr Burgess believes he has produced the first book of crosswords of the type that the vast majority of solvers prefer.

Every one of the 150 puzzles can be solved, he says, by Mr Everyman—and his wife. While they are graded according to the standard of the clues (*Definitely Not Difficult— Moderately Easy—Not So Easy—Easier Than They Look*) none is likely to appeal to the retired Reverend Erasmus Erudite, whiling away his leisure in a reference-book-lined study. On the contrary, every puzzle can be solved without consulting a dictionary or other reference book. The solver is not required to supply a word missing from some obscure quotation, or wrestle with any other abstruse devices. But the clues *are* spiced with that dash of ingenuity which makes solving crosswords the amusing and worthwhile pastime that it is. (2/6)